FOR A
SUCCESSFUL
LIFE

Bas Haring

Translated by
Paul Vincent

**Beautiful
Books**

This translation first published 2008 by

Beautiful Books Limited
36-38 Glasshouse Street
London W1B 5DL
www.beautiful-books.co.uk

Originally published in the Netherlands as *Voor een echt succesvol leven*
by Uitgeverij Nijgh & Van Ditmar

ISBN 9781905636310

9 8 7 6 5 4 3 2 1

A catalogue reference for this book is available from
the British Library.

Cover design by Ian Pickard.
Front cover and inside illustrations by Mark Patterson.
Typesetting by Ellipsis Books Limited, Glasgow.
Printed and bound in the UK by CPI Mackays, Chatham ME5 8TD

A friend of mine wasn't a bit surprised that this book had taken me so long: 'It doesn't strike me as very motivating, writing a book about why there's no need to write books.' I have to admit he's right. Yet I still enjoy writing books. It's the most enjoyable thing there is, thinking about what really concerns me and trying to put my thoughts on paper; on paper because paper is so much clearer than the spoken word, or TV, which is completely ephemeral.

Whatever you may think of the notion that, more than you expect and more than you find comfortable, you are a small part of a continuing greater whole – an onward-hurtling mechanism – I still believe in that notion. And I think it's important for me to tell you about it. Because the mechanism is not there for your benefit.

Whether I've succeeded in my aim and been clear enough, I don't know. But even if I haven't succeeded, I'd like to thank a number of people:

Anske van Luijtelaar – for her precise and well-thought-out comments on my idea, and for our excellent collaboration.

Janne Willems – for her terrific commitment and fresh eyes, and also for our excellent collaboration.

Arie Verhagen – for reading the first draft, and for his comments.

The Netherlands Institute for Advanced Study in the Humanities and Social Sciences – a wonderful place to work: an oasis of calm, interest and modesty.

Leiden University – for their patience.

Daniel Dennett – to whose thinking I owe a great deal – for allowing me to work in his office for a month.

Harry Starren – who has the Netherlands' best – seaborne! – hotel for working in.

Staas de Jong – for the story about Eddie Slovik.

Media Technology students at Leiden University – for the feedback they gave me on a rather confused lecture.

1

John & Annie

The characters in this picture don't really exist – let me call them John & Annie. They come from an advertising poster, but they might just as well have really existed. They pose proudly beside their new fridge full of fruit, milk and beer. They have a 'really successful' life, and the fridge bears witness to this.

Poor John & Annie. They really seem to think that fridges and success are the same thing. We know better, we know that John & Annie are gullible victims of TV commercials and junk mail. They don't know that themselves, otherwise they would never have posed so proudly next to their new fridge. What's more, their illusion isn't an innocent one; John has started a second job and Annie has taken out a high-interest loan: all for that fridge. Poor John & Annie: they're scrimping and saving for something that's not true, and they don't even know it.

But John & Annie raise a tricky question. If they don't know they're gullible victims and are scrimping and saving for something that's not true, then how do we think we know that the things *we* scrimp and save for are true? We may not pose next to the fridge, but we do have countless beliefs that demand our time, money and energy.

I have a problem with them too. For instance, with the belief that I must achieve something in my life: leave something behind, partly in the form of books. Well, I enjoy writing books, but it's not the only thing that matters to me. If the writing were all that mattered, I could have set light to the manuscript once I'd finished it. But I didn't; otherwise you wouldn't have read this. I want to publish my books, so badly that I sacrifice my holidays to them and lie awake at nights if the writing doesn't flow for a while. Why is that? How do I get it into my head that I must deny myself in order to be read?

And I'm not the only one who scrimps and saves. Athletes trade the best years of their lives for a few medals. Schoolchildren do paper rounds for Nike instead of Primark trainers, and employees suffer stress and heart attacks on their way to the top. How sensible is all this? And why do we do it? Are we perhaps – like John & Annie – gullible victims in pursuing our dreams and success?

I think we are. At any rate more often than we'd like.

What would an outsider make of us? What would a Martian think, or someone from the Middle Ages, or a Congolese encountering us for the first time? Would he or she think we've all got it made? 'Well, well, those people drive nice cars, have a nice life, great health care; what more do they want?' Or would he take a more thoughtful approach and think: 'My oh my, the speed those people move at! What are they all after and where are they all going?' I don't know what an outsider would think, but probably it's mixture of the two.

This book isn't a manual for a 'really successful life'. On the contrary – put it back on the display while you still can! If you can. This book tries precisely to put success in perspective. How sensible is it for us to pursue success? Instead, for example, of happiness or the feeling of 'being comfortable in our own skin'. Do we really pursue that success for ourselves, or because it's hard for us to do anything else?

To be honest, success is only one of the topics surveyed in this book. I chose the title mainly because of that hilarious poster of John & Annie and as an ironic coun-terweight to the many books on success surrounding us: 'Seven Steps to Success', 'Successful Leadership' and 'Success without a Degree'. Those kinds of books.

Only after a long detour will I reach the topic of 'the successful life'. In large part this book is concerned with things that are good at surviving as opposed to things that are doomed to extinction. How this links to success will eventually become clear to you. What characterises the things that survive? Are the things that disappear inferior to what survives? I shall give examples of splendid things that have nevertheless disappeared: the dodo, my local patissier and a Dutch anarchist group of the 1960s. I shall also give examples of things that are good at surviving, but aren't that great.

After that I shall inquire whether there may also be ideas – or notions, beliefs: things in our head – that may be good at surviving, but aren't good for us to have. Perhaps our idea of pursuing success, reaching the top, is one such idea. And finally this book also tries to put in a good word for the exceptional people who don't necessarily lead a successful life, who are content with a life of pure patience. Perhaps I should try that too. But first a story that sums up the gist of this book, a story about my ducks.

2

The etymology of success

The essence of this book can perhaps best be illustrated with reference to my ducks. My partner and I have two ducks – one male and one female. Small white ducks with orange beaks, the Donald Duck variety. They swim in a ditch alongside our house and come by once or twice a day. They start quacking very loudly and want food. They do it in the morning – just after sunrise – and so every day I stand out in the garden in my bathrobe feeding ducks. I can recognise their quack from among thousands and the merest hint of a quack is enough – I sit up in bed and run downstairs. 'The ducks are here,' I say enthusiastically to my partner. She goes on sleeping.

Up to a few months ago we saw the ducks at least once a day. But at a certain moment only the male came by. The female seemed to have disappeared. Very occasionally she would come charging towards us from a long way off, start quacking furiously, gulp some food down and race back to the ditch.

'What's the matter with that funny duck?' I wondered. But I realised quite quickly that our duck was probably brooding somewhere. That turned out to be the case. On one occasion I followed her after she'd dropped by and found that she was hiding in the hedge of the house behind us, brooding about ten eggs.

Of course I was proud of our duck: a little duck like that sitting on ten eggs. But I also felt rather sorry for her; brooding didn't strike me as much fun. For four weeks on end a duck sits on her eggs and in the process loses a lot of weight. She scarcely eats and seldom leaves her eggs. Is that good for her health? I wondered.

'Is it good for my duck to lose so much weight?' A crucial question in this book – except that this book isn't just about ducks, but also about me, and about you. My first reaction would be 'no': it's not good for ducks to lose weight. Losing weight is unhealthy. An emaciated dog is given extra food by animal welfare organisations and teenagers who lose weight deliberately are sent to a psychologist.

'But why would my duck do something that's not good for her?' is the next logical question. And the answer is obvious: the eggs of ducks that don't brood for 28 days don't hatch. My duck has to starve herself for four

weeks, or she won't get any ducklings. Not that my duck is aware of this: she probably hasn't the faintest idea why she's sitting on those eggs and scarcely eating. But ducks that don't brood don't get ducklings. Ducks like that become extinct. The only duck that survives is the duck that does not leave her nest for 28 days – and hence loses weight.

'*But is it really terrible for my duck to lose so much weight?*' On closer inspection the answer has to be 'no' – despite my initial intuition that it struck me as hard on such a duck. Although an emaciated duck looks unhealthy, it's nowhere near as bad as it looks: she doesn't die. Apart from that, ducks probably don't mind not eating for four weeks. It wouldn't surprise me at all to find that they loved spending 28 days on a nest. Four weeks with nothing at all on your mind but eggs.

Fortunately nature is so generous that my duck isn't too upset about sitting on the nest for four weeks. And that stands to reason: if she had found it so awful she would have been very tempted to stop brooding. The only duck that survives is not only the duck that doesn't leave its nest for 28 days; it's also the duck that doesn't mind too much.

'*So what am I going on about?*' True, the duck loses weight, but it doesn't kill her and besides, she probably doesn't mind too much. What is there against this, or why is this interesting? Why should this story be so central to this book?

Well ... and I think that's the essence of what I'm trying to say, the ducks that *don't* lose weight, don't sit on the nest for 28 days, don't feel like it or whatever, these ducks are not inferior ducks. They're certainly no worse off. Indeed, there's something to be said for such a duck – a duck like that stays nice and plump instead of going thin as a rake. I can't disagree with the duck that thinks: 'No way, scarcely anything to eat for 28 days and what do I get at the end of it? Kids! Kids I have to look after. Count me out.' Not that ducks think or talk, but I'm pretending for a moment.

It's the same line of reasoning I described in an earlier book. Then it concerned gay people. Gay people don't have children. Gay people don't transmit anything to the next generation, or at any rate they don't contribute to the creation of the next generation. But... that doesn't detract in any way from the significance of a gay person's life. His or her life is just as pleasant or valuable as anyone else's. It's just that after a gay couple 'things grind to a halt'.

'Why do you always focus on children so much?' gay people have sometimes objected. 'I may not be able to have children. But surely I can leave something behind in another way? Be successful? Maybe I'll write a book one of these days. My life can definitely have a meaning for people who come after me!'

Yes, that's true, but my point is precisely that you don't have to. There's absolutely no *need* to leave anything behind or achieve anything. Just as the duck that leaves no other ducks behind is an excellent duck, so the person who has absolutely no significance for the course of history may be an excellent person. To my mind. Perhaps even enviable, just as the duck that doesn't lose weight may also be enviable.

For me this story always evokes the image of a dead-end street. A duck that doesn't lose weight is heading down a dead-end street; after her, no more ducklings. But there's nothing wrong with dead-end streets: they can be the most wonderful streets. It stands to reason that there are few such streets; but the fact that there are few of them doesn't make them any less valuable.

What survives is not in itself better than what stops. That's more or less the essence of this book. There are wonderful things that stop of necessity, and sometimes the ugliest things survive.

'Yes, but hold on, this is all a bit simplistic; what do you mean, for instance, by "better"? What's that?' Well, I'll come back to that later. If I could have written the answer down right away, this book would only have been about five pages long.

'And what on earth has this got to do with "success"? Or with "the successful life"?' Well, something odd is happening with the meaning of the word 'success'. What does 'success' mean to you? My educated guess would be that it has a positive connotation. Success is good: a successful cake is a good cake. What's more, success isn't just good, it's good for you – which is why there are so many books on sale on the subject.

The funny thing is that 'success' comes from the Latin *succedere*. The main meaning of *succedere* is 'follow on from, take the place of'. Originally 'success' meant something like 'succession' – though originally means a very long time ago: some time in the Middle Ages. Inheritance tax is payable on an inheritance by the heirs or 'successors', and 'successive' means 'following in order'. How all this came about is not completely clear to me, but it's curious. Having succession, success, has come to mean the same as what is good for you; something you want.

Yet success in the original sense isn't good for you at all. Your successors are less good for you than you are for them. The inheritance you bequeath is not for you. The heirs are to be envied, not you. The etymology of the word 'success' reveals a hidden meaning in the word. A meaning that in my view still percolates to some extent into what we mean by 'success' today.

A successful book is a book that is read.

A successful company is not yet bankrupt.

A successful idea is an idea that catches on.

And a successful life is a life that has set something in motion. A life that doesn't run into a cul-de-sac, but is part of a through road. Success goes on: that's implicit in the meaning of the word. But I find the unsuccessful life, life in a dead-end street, a very nice life too.

Success is different from happiness. Happiness is good for the person who has it, but I don't know if success is always good for the person who has success. I've heard people say often enough 'When I was less successful, I was happier.' They're obviously different things. Indeed, sometimes success goes hand in hand with pain. 'You have to suffer to succeed' sounds like the daily mantra of a football coach, while 'You have to suffer to be happy' is a statement a masochist might make.

Just as brooding ducks go on and produce new brooding ducks, so success goes on, fuelling new success. That is also implicit in the etymology of the word. Just as I wonder whether the brooding duck is to be envied, so I wonder whether the successful person is to be envied.

I have the feeling that in our striving after success we are a little like my duck. That doesn't sound very well-substantiated: 'I have the feeling that...' There are undoubtedly lots of objections that can be made against my argument. Nevertheless my reflections and doubts are interesting enough to share with you – I think. I can at least demonstrate that ugly things sometimes survive, and that dead-end streets can be the most beautiful. Which street would you rather walk down: an ugly through road, or a beautiful cul-de-sac?

☞ **Biologically speaking, brooding ducks and heterosexuals form part of a through road, but as individuals they are not in themselves any better off than non-brooding ducks and homosexuals.**

☞ **Just as ducks that do not brood are not inferior ducks and homosexuals are not inferior people, the unsuccessful life – the life that has set nothing in motion – can be a wonderful life.**

3

Everything comes to an end

Everything comes to an end. Well, most things do. I don't know if the number two will ever come to an end – to give one example. In the sense that I wonder whether the number two will ever cease to exist. Or gravity: will it ever stop? But most things do – almost nothing goes on forever.

What ensures that things survive? What is their secret? But first: what does survive actually mean? I won't waste too many words on this, just a few.

If something ever was and is still there, it has survived. And it will continue to do so until it's disappeared. My car survives until it winds up on the scrap heap. The original exhaust, though, survived for a much shorter time – only a few months. But the Lada make won't disappear when my car is crushed for scrap – my car is a Lada. Lada won't disappear until all the factories close, no one sells Ladas any longer and there are no more Ladas to be found – apart from a few in museums.

Some things last longer than others. I hope to keep my Lada for about ten years, though my previous car lasted only four: I wrote it off. My model of Lada has been going for over 25 years and Lada itself since the 1960s. The car – the vehicle in the general sense – has in turn existed much longer than Lada and will last much longer. Probably.

Suppose you have something that you don't want to lose – I'll leave aside what for now. You want it to go on. In that case you have, roughly speaking, three ways of achieving that aim:

1 *You make it indestructible.*
2 *You maintain it well.*
3 *You make copies of it.*

Not all those ways work equally well for everything. Way one is the megalith method. Megaliths like those at Stonehenge are indestructible and last for ages. They've been there for several thousand years and will hold out for a while longer. The method is not very effective for cars. To be honest I can scarcely imagine a Lada with the same qualities as a megalith. A truly inde-structible car is an impossibility: it would never move from the spot.

Way one is also the way of atoms. An oxygen atom – to take an example – isn't easy to destroy. The oxygen atoms on earth date back several billion years – much further than megaliths – and even when the earth disappears oxygen atoms will remain oxygen atoms. Funny idea, really.

Way two is the one I use myself: maintenance. I maintain myself. I eat and drink, and move occasionally. In this way I make sure my body refreshes itself; replaces old cells with new. In that way I hope to keep going for eighty years or so. Not as long as a megalith, but still quite a while. If I didn't look after myself, I would disappear just like that.

For cars method two would work in theory, though it is rather impractical to have to send the car to the garage for maintenance every day or every week. That does, however, happen with planes: they're maintained tremendously well and in principle can last for ages. That doesn't happen because at a certain moment more modern planes offer all kinds of advantages over older ones: they can fly faster, more economically, with less noise-pollution, and so on. In any case at a certain moment it becomes practical to replace old aircraft with new ones. But planes could last for ages.

Way three – making copies – is a clever way. It works mainly for things that are easy to copy. For cars it isn't that suitable: it's quite a job making a copy of a Lada, unless you happen to be Lada and have the use of a Lada factory. Furthermore, it raises the question whether a copy of my Lada is still the same Lada. But for information, photos, music and stories method three is terrific.

If you want to keep a photo, the best thing to do is to make a couple of prints and store them in different places. In that way the photo will survive for some time. That's what I do with my stories – books, columns, articles. I'm terrified that at a certain moment I'll lose them. Carving them onto a megalith is not an option.

With my first book I thought 'Oh, that's on paper. It'll last forever.' But that was a big mistake.

I lost the original manuscript during a move, the book had virtually disappeared from bookshops, and I had long since given away my own copies. Fortunately I still had a text file. I now keep various copies of that file spread over various computers, one as far away as the United States. It struck me as a good idea.

It would be even cleverer if I were to set up the text file of my first book in such a way that it periodically deposited a copy of itself on some stray computer. Of course not too blatantly or aggressively, or the file would be tracked down and subsequently destroyed. Quietly parking a copy somewhere, though, is a good way of surviving. Method three.

Organisms – individual plants and animals – survive through method two, and species survive through method three: a cow lasts for years because it maintains itself – or is maintained; cows as a species have lasted so long because individual cows make copies of themselves. True, they're not perfect copies, but they're good enough to be called 'cow'. Exactly the same applies to Ladas: the individual Lada lasts for a while because it's maintained and the Lada make lasts because new Lada copies continuously appear on the market.

Animals that don't maintain themselves disappear, and if they don't copy themselves either the whole species disappears. Emperor moths are particularly bad at maintaining themselves. They don't even eat. Emperor moths are doomed to disappear – not surprisingly they live only a few days or weeks. But they reproduce all the more intensively – it's actually all they do. So the Emperor moth still exists – and the Emperor moth caterpillar.

We don't see things that are bad at surviving all that often. The point is that most of those types of things have already disappeared. Things that aren't indestructible, aren't maintained and of which no new copies are produced – such things disappear. Astatine atoms, to give one example, unlike oxygen atoms, last only a few minutes. That's why astatine is so rare: by the time you've found it it's already gone.

For the same reason we see few Simcas nowadays. When I was young the place was crawling with Simcas: cheap French cars that were ten a penny, and looked it. Almost two million Simca 1000s — the best-known model — were produced. But Simcas were rather prone to rust. Maintenance couldn't stop it. Simcas were bad at surviving and they didn't. The Citroën DS dates from the same period, and there are still plenty around today. They rust less and they're often well looked after. About 300,000 fewer Citroën DSs were made than Simca 1000s, but DSs are still all over the place, whereas I haven't seen a Simca for years.

Cars, houses, foodstuffs, books, plants and animals. Most things around us are quite good at surviving. Excuse my using the word 'things'. Cars and houses may be things, but plants and animals aren't, and foodstuffs aren't usually either. Yet I like to use the word 'things'. As a kind of general receptacle.

'Yes, but bread doesn't last all that long, does it? Or a glass of milk? A few days, and it's either gone or it's gone off.'

A loaf doesn't last very long, that's true, nor does a glass of milk. But for every loaf that disappears another appears in its place, and for every glass of milk too.

Bread in general does last, as does milk. Bread has existed for thousands of years and will probably go on existing for a while.

There are loads of things that have had a relatively short existence: hula hoops, WAP (Wireless Application Protocol), checked golfing trousers, the Kermit telephone – a half-hearted mobile telephone system that began in 1992 and lasted less than seven years. All those things are rare now. Most things around us are good at surviving, in at least one of the three ways. Mountains, atoms and megaliths are all indestructible and that's why they're still there. (Rembrandt's *Nightwatch*, though, isn't indestructible in itself, but is relatively indestructible because it is well guarded by attendants.) Roads, houses and aircraft are always maintained, and so continue to exist. And while loaves, pencils and socks may not last all that long, new copies are constantly appearing.

A nice example of something that will always remain rare again comes from my ducks. In fact my partner and I have a family with ducks. That's quite rare: most people have a family with children. Families with children are much more common than families with ducks; not that families with children are nicer, but because families with children often produce new families with children. Nice families with children make copies of themselves: 'It used to be such fun when I came home from school on Wednesday afternoons. Having tea with my mother in the kitchen and telling her what had happened that day. I want that too later, with my own children.'

A nice family with children can easily produce a nice new family with children; but a nice family with ducks doesn't have the same effect at all. However nice my family is, and however sweet my ducks, I've never yet given anyone the idea of founding a family with ducks – except perhaps now.

Nice families with children reproduce themselves. Yet nice families with children are no nicer than nice families with ducks, at least not for me. Nevertheless the latter are doomed to remain rare, while nice families with children will probably last a while longer.

So why were you forced to read all that? Well, because in this book I'm addressing the question of whether what goes on, is successful, is better than what stops. In that case it's only logical first to examine the nature of the things that go on or survive.

☞ The things that don't disappear at once, but survive for a while are either indestructible, or are well-maintained, or regularly copied.

☞ Most things around us are relatively good at surviving. The things that were not good at it have disappeared in the meantime.

☞ Apologies for the word 'things'.

4

Does the best come out on top?

Things continue to exist through maintenance, copies or toughness, but are such things better than the things that disappear? That would be nice: things that survive are more widespread than things that disappear and of course it's nice when better things are more widespread than inferior ones. Besides, it would be rather sad if the inferior survived and the superior disappeared – leaving aside for a moment what exactly I mean by 'superior' and 'inferior'.

Fortunately it's often the case that the superior survives at the expense of the inferior: Trabant has disappeared while BMW lives on. Arsenal are still going strong, but Luton Town went bankrupt; short-necked giraffes have become extinct, while their long-necked counterparts are still roaming free. The superior won out against the inferior. But I don't think that always happens. I don't believe that the things that last longest are necessarily the best. I don't believe that 'being good' and 'being good at surviving' are the same thing. The good sometimes survives, but at other times it disappears just as fast in favour of the less good. In fact the last story about my ducks was an example: nice families with ducks are doomed to disappear or remain rare, though they're not any less nice than nice families with children.

A much nicer example from my childhood: PK chewing gum.

PK chewing gum was great chewing gum, but it no longer exists. My father used to chew it in the old days. Every morning before he cycled to work he'd take a piece of PK chewing gum for the journey. I was almost never given chewing gum by my father. He didn't think you should chew gum at school, and he was probably right, but there were boys in my class who did chew gum. Not PK chewing gum, but the Sportlife brand. I thought it was very odd that the boys in my class chewed a different gum from my father, and that's probably why I noticed the brand.

Later the brand became even more noticeable. Through the large, striking ads in papers and magazines. Later still there were even television and cinema commercials. Expensive ads, ads featuring skiers and snowboarders who were transported to remote mountain tops and then skied fearlessly down to the bottom. There they took off their expensive sunglasses and chewed a piece of gum.

How are all those helicopters, sunglasses and camera teams being paid for? I wondered. Not that I wondered this consciously when I was ten, but I did have a vague, puzzled feeling of 'I don't get it' from the first moment I saw a Sportlife commercial.

Should Sportlife commercials not be familiar to you, you probably know the brand from the flashy packaging placed right by the checkout in the supermarket; you can't miss it. Whereas my father's PK chewing gum came in a small, squarish packet that you could easily put in your pocket, Sportlife comes in a large de luxe box filled mostly with air. The individual pieces are separately mounted on a large plastic strip. How on earth can the costs of that de luxe packaging and those expensive ads be found? I wondered. It seemed to me that a packet of Sportlife should cost over four euros – but Sportlife actually cost about 20 eurocents.

At present Sportlife costs about 70 eurocents, some 11 cents of which is duty and 20 per cent is the retailer's profit, leaving 40 per cent for the manufacturer of Sportlife. One 13-gram packet of chewing gum (which is what the packets weigh) costs approximately 5 cents in raw materials, about half of which goes on the gum – cost 2 euros per kilo. Add some miscellaneous overheads for a factory, staff and transport, and you're left with at least 30 cents or so per packet available for advertising. They can afford quite a few skiers, helicopters and camera crews out of that.

So that's what you're paying for. When you buy Sportlife, you're not buying chewing gum, you're buying advertising. And why do you buy Sportlife instead of another chewing gum? Because you know Sportlife from the ads, or because Sportlife comes in those big packets that are much more eye-catching than those small, cheap packets of PK. A kind of vicious circle that you unthinkingly perpetuate – as long as you chew Sportlife chewing gum: you're paying for advertising, and you do so… because of the advertising.

In this way Sportlife ensures that it survives. In a certain sense the chewing gum uses you for its own ends, and so it still exists. Unlike PK, which has been impossible to find in the supermarket for the past ten years. Except, it seems, in one small shop in the provinces. I imagine the owner of the shop in question must have once picked up an old consignment of PK chewing gum at a knock-down price.

So now the sixty-four-thousand-dollar question: Is Sportlife better than PK? Because we were talking about the difference between 'being good' and 'being good at surviving'. That is not such an easy question:

Turbo Clean

*washes whiter,
does 0-60mph in 7 seconds
and 25 miles per gallon!*

when is one thing better than another? My first reaction would be: Of course Sportlife isn't better than PK. Precisely the opposite: that nice, honest and modest PK was much better than that flashy Sportlife! That reaction, though, may be a bit simplistic. It's more sensible and simpler to ask *as what* one thing is better than another. A car is not better than a packet of washing powder. However, *as a means of transport* a car definitely is better – just as a packet of washing powder is better for washing with. Sportlife is better at surviving at any rate, because for the time being Sportlife has survived and PK hasn't: Sportlife is better *as a survivor*. But is Sportlife also better *as chewing gum*? I don't think so. Chewing gum is first and foremost for chewing and in that respect PK and Sportlife are as good as each other. The reason that Sportlife still exists is due not so much to the quality of Sportlife as chewing gum as to the fact that Sportlife knows how to sell itself – through those expensive ads and eye-catching packaging. That is definitely a quality, but a different quality from 'being a good chewing gum'. Sportlife might just as well have been a hair gel: a substance that snowboarders dropped off by helicopter put on their hair at the foot of the mountain.

As chewing gum Sportlife is no better than PK. But there are other questions that you might ask. *For whom* is Sportlife better than PK? Well, at any rate Sportlife isn't better *for you*. When you buy Sportlife, you're paying for something you don't really want. You want chewing gum, but you're paying for snowboarders. That's not good for you.

'You're wrong,' an advertising man once objected. 'Sportlife isn't chewing gum at all. That's not what people pay for when they buy Sportlife. People buy an illusion, the illusion of snowboarding, snow-covered mountains, helicopters and macho sunglasses – and all that for only 70 eurocents. For no more than 70 eurocents people have a momentary sensation of being on a skiing trip. *As an illusion* Sportlife is much better than PK. That was boring, insipid chewing gum.'

The man was probably quite right. Sportlife is indeed

a much better illusion than PK, but are you prepared to pay for that illusion? In the supermarket queue do you think 'Hey, I'm going to buy a packet of chewing gum?' Or do you think 'I'm going to pay 70 eurocents for the vague and short-lived illusion of being on a skiing holiday?' Personally I haven't got much money to spend on illusions, and when it turns out by accident that I'm paying for an illusion, I just think it's a waste of money and beat myself over the head.

'Yes but,' you could say, 'in economic terms Sportlife definitely is better than PK chewing gum, since PK is no longer on sale and Sportlife has been a big success.' You're quite right. At any rate within the economic system – the mechanism in which consumers buy, advertising people advertise, etc – Sportlife is better at surviving than PK. *As part of the economy* Sportlife is better than PK, but surely that doesn't mean that Sportlife is a better chewing gum?

The question 'Is X better than Y?' is a tricky one. What is 'better'? What is 'good' and what is 'bad'? Or 'What is good and bad?' to put it more grandly. It's much simpler to ask '*As what* is X better than Y?' or '*For whom* is X better than Y?'

As chewing gum Sportlife is no better than PK, and *for you* it's no better either – or for me. Still, PK disappeared and Sportlife remained. What's more, Sportlife still exists *thanks to you* – and me. That's not a very pleasant feeling: not good for me, but still thanks to me.

Sportlife really isn't an exceptional case. What, to take just one example, is the best shoe? In my opinion it's one that fits well, is long-lasting, hard-wearing and is given away free. I can scarcely imagine a better shoe. But that's not the shoe we wear. I'd go further: take a shoe out of the wardrobe and it will probably be the opposite of the best conceivable shoe. The shoes we have last only a short time: if they haven't worn out within a few months then they go out of fashion after a while; and we pay a fortune for them.

Just for the record: I'm not trying to sell you a pair of Mephistos – timeless German health shoes that ten years ago looked the same as they will look in ten years' time and will also last that long. I wear the same kind of fashion shoes as everyone else. I'll go further: I have twenty pairs of shoes and buy at least four new pairs every year. But there's no way the stacks of shoes I have are the best conceivable shoes.

☞ **The question whether one thing is better than another is a tricky one. It's easier to ask *as what* one thing is better, or *for whom*.**
☞ **The things that survive are certainly better as survivors than the things that disappear, but whether they are better in any other respect remains to be seen.**
☞ **There are things that survive thanks to me but that are not good for me.**

Sportlife is just an innocuous example. It gets trickier with more serious matters. Are there things that are not very good for us, but that we, perhaps unconsciously, perpetuate? Or, and this may sound like an odd idea, could there be such things as 'Sportlife ideas'? Ideas that we have, that are not terribly helpful for us to think, but which we perpetuate, precisely by thinking them? – just as we perpetuate Sportlife by buying it. I understand that sounds rather odd: as if the thoughts we think were comparable with chewing gum. But I actually do believe that such Sportlife ideas exist. Ideas that are not particularly helpful to us, but that survive in our heads because we think them and act in accordance with them. I'll come back to that later. But first a brief look at the relationship between 'being good' and 'being good at surviving'. They're not the same, but there is definitely *a* relationship. If Sportlife had tasted of cardboard it would no longer have existed: absolute shit becomes extinct. There are, though, a number of questions that can be asked about the relationship between 'good' and 'surviving':

Is survival good in itself? Is it good that the things that exist should survive? I have the impression that lots of people would say 'yes'. Not that they believe that everything should survive – they'd be quite happy for corruption to disappear – but we think it's a shame when many things cease to exist. Some people get very upset about the decline of Irish Gaelic in Ireland. 'Don't you agree it would be a disaster if soon there's no one left who says "baoi fri" or "uisge bheatha"?' I personally don't see it like that: why should that be a disaster? Nor is it, surely, a disaster that no one still uses old-fashioned words like 'anon' (soon) or

'Zounds!' (God's wounds!), except jokingly. In my view survival *in itself* is not something good.

Are there good things that cannot *survive*? Definitely, I'm convinced of it. Actually, PK was an example. Excellent as chewing gum and also very good for me, with its modest, honest packaging. Then of course there are nice families with ducks. Just as nice as nice families with children, but they will always lead a marginal existence – they're not 'survivors'.

Actually this is what I get upset about: things that necessarily disappear and that nevertheless can be beautiful. I have more examples...

5

On beautiful things that pass

There are lots of beautiful things that don't have it in them to survive, that are doomed to disappear. I have no crystal-clear criteria for determining what's beautiful and what's ugly, or what's good and what's less good, but I can at least go by my personal taste and what's more I can say *as what* something is good, or *for whom*.

The best-known example of something beautiful that has disappeared is the dodo. A splendid, sweet-natured bird, a bit of a dope, an easy-going fatso that scraped a living and was totally unsuspecting. Until the Dutch arrived, in the sixteenth century. I imagine that the poor creatures ran to meet the Dutch out of curiosity – in the hope of being fed or something.

They were sitting ducks. Three shots, three bull's-eyes. It seems dodos weren't all that tasty, but tasty enough, or enough fun to shoot, since within a few decades they were completely extinct, blown away by the Dutch.

It was a little too good to be true: an idyllic population of sociable souls. That's asking for trouble; it can't survive.

And if something of the kind does survive, it's on an island. The dodo lived on Mauritius; the equally dopey kiwi lives in New Zealand; and the koala on the great island of Australia. Islands are the only place where exceptionally peaceful creatures can continue their exceptionally peaceful existences for a while. Until the Dutch arrive, or other predators; then the game is up.

Try releasing a few predators on sixteenth-century Mauritius and all succeeding generations of dodos will have stressful lives. The predators will gorge on these walking larders and they will thrive. But for the dodo things will get harder and harder. Should the dodo as a species survive the arrival of the predator, the only dodos to survive will be those who run away at the slightest noise and hide in the undergrowth. From a fat friendly softy the dodo will degenerate into a lean, muscular, stressed-out neurotic.

The reverse doesn't apply. Take a few dodos to an island full of tigers and nothing at all will happen; but take a few tigers to an island full of dodos and the fat will be in the fire. A stressful life of great pressure, hassling and being hassled is more stable than the calm, easy-going life of the dodo; it's better at surviving.

If you ask me the good has disappeared and the bad has come out on top: I prefer a world of easy-going dodos to a world of stressed-out neurotics. But the latter survive, and the former doesn't.

Another example: the baggage conveyor belt at Heathrow or any big airport. The conveyor belt that always takes you so long. A whole planeload of people converge on 30 metres of conveyor belt. You peer between nervous tourists draped in souvenirs to catch a glimpse of your suitcase. Sometimes you have to stand on tiptoe, sometimes you have to kneel. When you eventually see your case you have to elbow your way hurriedly through the throng, because before you know it the case has gone again.

There is a more sensible way. If everyone keeps 10 metres away, everyone can see their baggage tumbling onto the belt. As your case inches past you move calmly forward, take it off the belt and walk back again, so as not to block other people's view. No one has to push and everyone sees their case immediately.

Until one awkward customer messes things up. One fellow-traveller who doesn't have his nerves under control – or doesn't understand the system – remains obstinately standing by the conveyor belt. Or perhaps he or she is just an anti-social type who can't stand all those well-behaved people standing 10 metres away. Others try grumpily to look round the dissident. 'Why doesn't that great lump step back a few metres?' And someone takes a step forward – because otherwise he can't see enough. 'What's he doing now?' the next person thinks. Then all hell lets loose: in no time everyone is pushing and shoving around the conveyor belt, and that's exactly what happens.

The ideal solution to the baggage conveyor belt exists, but disappears, slips through our fingers. The good disappears and the less good remains. That was one more example.

Another woeful disappearance: my local patissier, a wonderful craftsman from whom I often bought half a flan at the weekend to have with coffee. But the patissier has gone and you can't find flans anywhere. Except at Multi-Flan. There I can order flans round the clock online or on a freephone number. My flan is baked overnight in a big bakery producing nothing but flans – and it's with me the next morning. All completely automated. Multi-Flan is a well-oiled machine, perfect in every detail, and staff at the call centre don't even need to know that they're working for a flan company: as long as they follow the correct procedures, press the right buttons, tick the right boxes on forms, the right flan will be delivered, on time.

Isn't that convenient, and efficient! No baker can compete with that – and so they don't: Multi-Flan is the clear market leader in the 'flan field'.

Super-efficient organisations win out over inefficient, more 'bumbling' outfits. Lance Armstrong's cycle team is another example. It was a very tight organisation in which every rider had his specialised job: getting water, staying on someone's wheel or forcing the pace on a climb. Everyone stuck to their task, as if they were office workers rather than racing cyclists.

Amstrong's team prepared for the Tour de France with scientific precision, and during the Tour the team was a well-oiled machine, relentless and invincible, and sure enough: they won. Lance Armstrong is the only man ever to have won the Tour seven times. He did so at the expense of Jan Ullrich, who seems to be more talented but generally rode in more easy-going teams.

Is that good? Is it good that efficiency should win out over inefficiency?

For a start it's logical – the question whether it's good then immediately becomes less relevant. But I'd still like to dwell on it for a moment. The question should of course be: 'For whom?' For whom is it good or bad that efficiency should survive? For me as a customer it's good. It's good for me that my flan arrives on time and costs only 9 euros – instead of 19 at the patissier's.

But for the staff of those efficient companies it's not so good at all, I think. I wouldn't like being part of an efficient machine, and it's so boring too, so businesslike. It takes some of the fun out of it if everything has to be done so efficiently, and although the patissier around the corner was a typical small shopkeeper, it was nice chatting to him now and then. Very inefficient, all that chatting.

Inefficiency on the other hand is pleasant. I like inefficiency: it's also how I live my life. When I cook – which I love to do – I cook very inefficiently. I put potatoes on, think a bit about all the things I have to do next, and go into the garden to pick herbs. When I return from the garden I have to turn the potatoes off again – because I've fed the ducks or just been for a run. Then I still have to defrost the fish. How very inefficient. Wonderful! What a shame that my work has to be efficient.

So I'm not that fond of efficiency and although for me as a customer it's good that efficiency should win out over inefficiency, it's less good for me as an employee. The question arises what I am more: a customer or an employee?

I'm an employee for about eight hours a day; forty hours a week. That's a long time. If it's good for me as a customer that efficiency should survive, but it's bad for me as an employee, then it's bad for me for at least forty

THEY'RE POPPING UP ALL OVER THE PLACE!

FLAN-*u*-LIKE

hours a week. 46 weeks a year and forty years of my life. Efficiency, what a pain, and in exchange for that pain my flan costs me only 9 euros instead of 19. To be honest I'm not sure if I should be so happy about that.

If being stressed wins out over being laid-back, if bad solutions can win out over good ones, I don't know what's better: winning or losing. Then I start wondering whether the things that survive aren't automatically a little suspect.

One last example of something beautiful that has disappeared: the anarchist Provo movement (referred to below as 'the Dutch anarchist group'). This vague political grouping founded in the 1960s by a number of young Dutch left-wing philosophers, artists and activists who wanted to change the world by playful means. Of course they didn't succeed, but it was fun while it lasted. (If I'm to believe the tales told about them; I didn't experience it myself.) 'Vote Provo. It's a Hoot.' was the slogan with which they tried to win seats on Amsterdam Town Council.

The interesting thing about the anarchists was that they didn't want to be an organisation, a club. If you were a club, they argued, a lot of energy was wasted on internal squabbles and organisational problems: What kind of logo should we have? Who'll be secretary? How do we ensure we're still here in two years' time? That kind of thing. So they didn't want to be a club – but that was tricky. Just try forming an association of ten without being a club – it's almost impossible, certainly when you give yourselves a name and publish a magazine. In that case you're immediately 'something': a club or group. 'That lot are the club associated with that mag.'

They were attempting to do the splits in an impossible way. On the one hand they didn't want to be an identifiable group, with a name and an organisation; on the other hand they did want to achieve a few things, involving a number of people because it wasn't possible alone. Apart from that, if you want to win votes for the town council you need a name and an organisation, whether you like it or not.

It's a fundamental dilemma: an unorganised collection of nameless individuals, without a constitution, without a magazine, or anything, is nothing. At any rate it's not something we can name or put a stamp on. It's very difficult *not* to be an organisation when there are ten of you – or else before you know it you fall apart like loose sand.

Like a self-fulfilling prophecy the club that emphasises its being a club has a chance of surviving, while the club that denies its own existence will disappear. The latter consequently happened with the Dutch anarchist group. On 13 May 1967 they dissolved – or rather they didn't actually do that — another clever move. On the day in question they stressed the fact that they no longer existed as an organisation, that the name 'Provo' did not refer to an association with a constitution or that sort of thing, but they hoped that the ideas that they, more or less, stood for would percolate through into mainstream politics. Since then of course we've heard no more of the Dutch anarchist group. Exactly what ideas of theirs have percolated through I don't know — definitely not many.

That's the way it goes: a club that doesn't go in for maintenance, that doesn't affirm its own existence, will not survive but will disappear. That doesn't detract from the fact that such a 'club' may be a very interesting, good, or excellent club.

The Netherlands has over 250 recognised charitable institutions that are all after one thing: charitable income. Charity costs money and those institutions do not get that automatically. You can sit in your attic room and declare yourself a charitable institution; if no one knows you exist you won't have a penny to spend. So you need a logo and a name, advertising space and radio commercials, a secretary to coordinate things, and so on and so on.

Apart from that there are other charitable institutions that want money from the same pot, that support other good causes – and so it's shoulders to the wheel for the good cause and for the survival of the organisation.

It's logical, for heaven's sake, inevitable even: charitable organisations that don't look after themselves in any way disappear. Charitable organisations must advertise themselves, go out into the street and actively seek funds, must have a board of management, a secretary and a marketing department – and those things cost money, so much that often very little is left for charitable work. But what do you want? The charitable organisation that does nothing but charitable work has no name, no logo, is untraceable, unorganised and like the Dutch anarchist group: before you know it, it has vanished off the face of the earth.

But is the charitable organisation that does not disappear off the face of the earth automatically a better charitable organisation? The club that collects a thousand euros and spends a thousand euros, or the club that collects ten thousand euros and of that manages to spend 1100 euros? I don't know; but I do know that the former cannot look forward to a very long life. The organisation that does not look after itself disappears. Like the Dutch anarchist 'organisation' or – positively the last example – a certain Amsterdam student club (referred to hereafter as the student club).

The society was founded in 1951 as a user-friendly,

non-traditional society for students who wanted to join a society, but for whom it wasn't such a big deal. They drank beer, chatted and organised a few things, but the continued existence of the society didn't much interest the members. They didn't bother much about recruiting new members. And so, as a logical consequence, the society went under, in 1970. But that doesn't mean it was a bad or stupid student club. On the contrary: the members were delighted with it. Not just that: they did exactly what the society had been founded for, that is, beer-drinking and chatting. They achieved their objective splendidly; it's just that such societies disappear. The only societies that remain are those that – in whatever way – do their best to survive. To put it more strongly: the social club where it is never sociable because people are too busy recruiting new members can expect a longer life than the social club where there is nothing but sociability.

Where have we got with the argument? I'm trying to show or at least make plausible that we are like my duck, my duck that starves herself for four weeks on her nest. That behaviour is mainly interpretable as 'something that lasts' instead of something that is good for my duck. And so I wonder whether some of things we do or strive after aren't of the same kind. Good at lasting but not good for us. Meanwhile I've shown that the things that survive are not in themselves better things.

6

A lot of crab

I'd like to look closer at one example of something impractical that is nevertheless successful and survives, an example from biology. The example of the peacock's tail, a terribly long tail: about a metre and a half. 'What good is it to such a creature?' many people wonder. Very little, I can tell you right now. In fact, the tail mainly gets in the creature's way. Particularly if you realise that peacocks are originally woodland birds. Believe me, it's no joke fluttering through the under-growth dragging a metre and a half of feathers behind you.

Other examples similar to the peacock's tail are the long nose or head of the sperm whale: three or four metres long and weighing several thousand kilos. What use is such a big nose to such a creature? Again the answer is 'precious little'. Or the claw of the fiddler crab – a huge claw. How on earth do those creatures come by their heavy head, long tail or big claw? Why do they have them?

Let me use the crab as my example, though I could just as well have talked about the sperm whale, the peacock, the bowerbird, the mandrill or a whole bunch of other creatures. I'm telling the story not because I'm keen to talk about animals as such – though I certainly find that fascinating – but because the story behind the fiddler crab's big clumsy claw illustrates a mechanism that equips individual organisms with 'clumsiness'. Does such a mechanism operate in our human world too? is the logical follow-up question. Not only in relation to physical characteristics like tails, noses and claws, but in a more general sense. Is there a mechanism operating in our world that ensures that we do or want things that are inconvenient for ourselves, though that complex of activities and wishes is good at surviving? First, more about the crab.

I often go on holiday to small islands and very often they are islands in warmer regions, like the Philippines, Mauritius, Polynesia, those kinds of places. Those small islands are almost always teeming with crabs. Close to the shore, but also for a few hundred metres inland. They sit next to their burrows – as if waiting for something – and when you come along they dart into the burrow. Very funny little creatures.

Many of those crabs have one relatively large claw. Rather an odd sight, since it makes them asymmetrical, which you don't see that often. They are fiddler crabs, and you find them on most tropical coasts. 'Why do the creatures have one claw that is so big?' I've sometimes wondered, without giving it much further thought. 'It's probably useful to them, in some way I don't know,' was the standard answer I formulated in my head and that seemed to be all there was to say. A crab has legs to walk on, eyes to see with, and that claw must be good for something. So it seemed to me, until at a certain moment I saw a few of those crabs with really big claws. Half the body of those crabs seemed to consist of 'claw'. What's more, it struck me that the creatures did not use those claws for anything. They ate with their other, much smaller claw. That gigantic claw seemed mostly to get in the way. Indeed I once saw one of those crabs topple over onto its side, because of the great weight of its own claw. Mysterious. 'How on earth do those creatures come to have a big, awkward claw?' I wondered again.

The answer turned out to be that female fiddler crabs find those big claws a turn-on. They themselves have much handier, smaller claws, but the males must have those whoppers. So they think. The male with the biggest and flashiest claw pulls the most females, and that male will also have the most offspring.

The males among those offspring also have those big claws and the females in turn find big claws a turn-on: they inherit that from their parents. Perhaps there will be one son among them with an even larger claw – pure chance – who will of course in turn become the macho of all machos and be able to pull countless females.

So in the course of time the fiddler crab's claw has become larger and larger, just because the females find it exciting. And those poor males simply have to lug the thing about. Why it is these females were turned on by those big claws and not by big ears or small claws, for example, is not so important for now. But in any case it's clear how the fiddler crab came by its big claw, and it's not yet completely clear what exactly fiddler crab females see in those big claws. In schematic form:

1 Fiddler crab females can choose, and they choose the male with the biggest claw.
2 The males with the biggest claws are chosen most often and hence also have the largest number of offspring.
3 The males among those offspring in turn have those big claws − they inherit them from their fathers. The females in turn have the same preference for big claws − they inherit it from their mothers.
4 The sons with the biggest claws are again chosen most often, and so on. From generation to generation the fiddler crab claw grows to gigantic proportions.

I could have told exactly the same story about the peacock's tail, the head of the sperm whale, or the mandrill, with its blue wrinkled nose with a bright red stripe and yellow goatee − just because females love it. Or the comb of a cockerel and the huge beak of the toucan. I once saw a toucan in the wild in the tropics − just like those crabs. And when you see a bird like that, with that big beak, you can scarcely help wondering what on earth such a creature is supposed to do with it. Biologists still haven't cracked it, after over a hundred years of study. The beak can't really be much use to a toucan; otherwise the biologists would have discovered what it is.

The story behind the fiddler crab's big claw immediately raises a number of questions that I want to deal with shortly:

☞ Is that big claw really no use at all to such a crab?
☞ Could it equally well have been a big mouth, or a very big back leg?
☞ Or on the contrary a very small claw?
☞ Would the male actually be better off with a small claw?
☞ Why isn't the claw much, much bigger?
☞ And what happens to an exceptional female that chooses a male with a sweet little claw?

To start with question one: Is that big claw really no use at all to such a crab? Well, I find that a tricky question. To be honest I don't really know what use a big claw is to such a crab. Captivating females is one use. What use is a male with a big claw to a female? That's really not completely clear. It's a lot clearer what use its legs or eyes are to a crab.

To tell the truth I think you can say that such a claw mainly gets in the crab's way. Of course, a male crab can pull females with it, but it would have been nicer for him if he'd been able to do that with a smaller claw. As it is, he lugs around a gigantic thing that sometimes, would you believe, makes him fall over. Those female crabs could easily have gone for something completely different: very big eyes or a bright red backside. The claw isn't that important.

Still it remains a tricky question: the question whether such a big claw is good for such a crab. 'Of course it is,' because then he can pull females; or 'no,' because such a claw mainly gets in the creature's way.

In India beggars use the money they've managed to beg to have an arm or leg amputated – a healthy one, that is. By real doctors, it seems, in hospitals. Those beggars do that because without an arm or leg they can earn more money from begging. They earn back their investment in no time.

'Good for them!' you could say. 'Increases their earning power.' Apart from that, it's the beggars' own choice, and beggars certainly aren't stupid. But it's pretty awful. You could also say 'Bad for them; someone without an arm or a leg is worse off than someone with.' And I opt for the latter. The world in which it's sensible to have arms and legs amputated is not a great world. At any rate not for beggars.

And just as I feel sorry for beggars without an arm or a leg I feel sorry for crabs with claws that are far too big. The world is far from ideal for them.

The fiddler crab's big claw is not there *for the benefit of* the crab. Because the crab derives little benefit from it. Such a claw is good at surviving: it doesn't disappear; on the contrary, the crab claw has grown bigger and bigger in the course of time. But such a claw is not good, at any rate not for its owner.

Can't those crabs escape from this misery? The story began with the fact that female crabs quite simply go for males with big claws. But what if by chance a female should emerge that goes for small claws? What then?

Let's assume that such a female exists – for the sake of convenience I'll call her 'Mrs Crab'. Mrs Crab is an exceptional female with a knowledge of biology and knows how things work. Mrs Crab knows that in fact a male with a big claw is no good to her. A sweet male that looks after her and fetches lots of food – now he is some use. Mrs Crab feels rather sorry for her rather less intelligent crab girlfriends who stupidly go for one of those machos with a big claw. She herself prefers a pleasant, hardworking husband with – what difference does it make? – a slightly smaller claw.

How will things turn out for Mrs and Mr Crab?

Mrs and Mr Crab live happily ever after and have lots of children. Thus far no problem. The male children will have the same cute little claw as their father. Perhaps a little bigger or a little smaller, but in any case relatively small compared with the other male crabs of their generation. The boys – Mrs Crab's sons – will have a hard time of it with the girls. Because the girls aren't that fond of boys with small claws: they want big claws. Hopefully there will be some intelligent ladies like Mrs Crab around, otherwise the sons will remain lifelong bachelors. Mrs Crab won't have any grandchildren and her branch of the family will eventually disappear. If not after one or two generations, then after a few.

If Mrs Crab wants a lot of grandchildren then there's nothing for it but to conform to the taste of others and opt for the macho male. Even if she knows he's a drip. Or in other words: over time Mrs Crabs who choose the male with the biggest claw survive at the expense of ladies who make other choices. A shame perhaps, but that's the way of the world. The dissident lady crabs disappear, and the conformists survive.

The fiddler crab is, as it were, in a cleft stick: the male can do nothing but spend his life lugging around a claw that is far too big and the female can do nothing but choose such a male. What terrible luck.

To be honest I identify a little with Mrs Crab. In her place I would have done the same. If a male with a small claw is nicer, who needs grandchildren? Mrs Crab is choosing for herself and biologically will be unsuccessful. No successors for her: her branch will die out, however sensible she may be.

I fully agree with Mrs Crab, but she will remain an exception. This is a poignant truth about reality. There is a difference between what's good for Mrs Crab and what is good at surviving. Sensible exceptions like Mrs Crab die out. But that doesn't have to prevent the exceptional exception from going ahead and choosing for itself. So I won't survive then, or be a success.

☞ **Fiddler crab males have big claws because fiddler crab females like them.**
☞ **Fiddler crab females like big claws because other fiddler crab females like them too.**
☞ **The exceptional 'sensible' fiddler crab female that doesn't fancy such a big claw, dies out.**

So why were you obliged to read this? Where does that crab claw fit in? Because the history of the crab claw demonstrates that there is a mechanism operating in nature that equips crabs with features that are unhelpful to them. And believe me, those crabs are no exception. That fiddler crab claw, sperm whale head and peacock tail are not 'aberrations' of nature or freak duds. No, they are illustrations of a general process that equips organisms with features that are unhelpful to them, features that survive, but are not helpful for those possessing them.

Thank heavens it is not the only mechanism operating in nature. Fortunately the world is so constructed that in general the crab has helpful features: eyes, legs, a shell. All very helpful. But the world is also so constructed that crabs are saddled with unhelpful features, without being able to do a thing about it.

Furthermore, there is no evil genius or suchlike lurking anywhere that enjoys tormenting those fiddler crabs. It happens more or less of its own accord, with no guilty party. But that doesn't make it any less lousy. And the main question it raises is: 'Do those kinds of mechanisms operate with us too?' And I don't mean in the biological sense. I'm not searching for a literal translation of the process underlying that big fiddler crab claw: big breasts, backside or head, for example. I'm looking for parallels in a more general sense – and they do exist. The first thing that occurs to me is the strange story of the towers of San Gimigniano.

San Gimigniano is a small town in Tuscany where in the Middle Ages people built absurdly high towers. Thirteen of them remain, the highest of which is about fifty metres. San Gimigniano is sometimes called the Manhattan of Tuscany; you can imagine what it looked like when there were still 72 of the towers standing – because that was the original number. For every hundred inhabitants there was a tower about 50 metres high. Useful!

The way those towers came to be there is reminiscent of the story of the crab claw. They were built by families that wanted to use them to enhance their prestige. The higher the tower, the greater the prestige. And the families with the highest ones secured the most interesting jobs, the most lucrative trade agreements and the best political allies. Of course everyone who could afford it started building high towers.

At the beginning of the 'big tower craze' there was a point to those big towers. At that time there were storage spaces: the more storage space you had the bigger noise you were. But later they served no purpose. I don't even know if there was a way into such a tower.

How did people react to those high towers in San Gimigniano at the time? Did they think 'What utter nonsense, but I'd better join in or I'll lose prestige'? Or were they convinced that high towers really mattered? I fear it was the latter to some extent. These weren't simple cardboard towers, but projects that took decades and cost a bomb. I can imagine that the citizens of San Gimigniano really took those towers seriously. What's more, if you shrugged your shoulders at that nonsense, you were kissing goodbye to all kinds of privileges and so there was nothing for it but to join in the building.

Before I examine what that mechanism underlying fiddler crab claws, peacock tails and sperm whale heads can tell us about our world, I'd like to answer two questions about fiddler crabs. Just because I think they're intriguing questions and intriguing answers:

☞ **Could fiddler crab females have gone for a big mouth instead of a big claw? Or a big back leg?**
☞ **Or on the contrary for a very small claw?**

7

More crab

A little more about those fiddler crabs. You may be thinking: 'What need is there for that? I didn't buy a book on biology, did I?' You're right there, but I find the process underlying that crab claw *so* intriguing – a process that produces strange results: creatures with features that are not helpful to them. And apart from that it provides a nice introduction to the next topic: ideas, notions, beliefs that have the quality of being good at surviving, but may not be so good to have.

Fiddler crab males, then, have such a big claw because female crabs love them, and females love them because the other females love them. In fact, the claw itself doesn't matter all that much. The females could just have well gone for big eyes or a big red patch. But could crab females also have fallen for the male with the smallest claw? Seems logical: if in what I was talking about a few pages ago you replace the word 'big' with the word 'small' it reads just as easily: Fiddler crab males have such terribly small claws because lady fiddler crabs find small claws a turn on. The man with the smallest claw pulls most females, with the result that in the course of time more and more fiddler crabs appear with very small claws. From generation to generation the fiddler crab claw shrinks, until it degenerates into a paltry stump.

Could this have been true? Could the fiddler crab claw just as easily have been a tiny stump? The answer is 'no'. Because there is a fundamental difference between 'big' and 'small'. For a start big can always get bigger, but small can't always get smaller. The very smallest claw is not a claw at all and there's nothing smaller than not a claw. Whereas a larger claw than the very largest claw does exist, or at any rate could exist.

Female crabs have to make a choice – they can't go off with every male – and that choice must be based on *something*. If they were to choose the male with the smallest claw the crab claw would shrink from generation to generation until it disappeared. At that point the females will have nothing to choose from: quite simply, none of the males will have a claw.

Imagine that once – millions of years ago – female crabs fell for small claws. Quite possible. Then it would have taken only a few generations and none of the males would have had a claw left. And what then? How would the females be able to make a choice? Something else would have replaced the claw. They would have chosen the shortest legs, the biggest yellow whatsit on their forehead or on the contrary the longest legs.

The choice for the smallest disappears at a certain moment – and is replaced by another choice. Whereas the choice for the biggest survives. Because there is nothing smaller than the smallest, but there is something bigger than the biggest. But that doesn't mean that big is also better. The preference of fiddler crabs for small claws disappears, while the preference for big claws survives. But that doesn't mean that big claws are really more use to lady – and gentlemen – crabs than small ones.

Yet another example of something that isn't good but is good at surviving. A big claw is no better than a small one. At any rate not *as a claw,* or *for its owner.* So choosing a bigger claw is not a better choice than choosing a smaller one, but the choice for a bigger one survives, while the choice for a smaller one is doomed to disappear.

Furthermore it's not helpful to choose the smallest, because smallness isn't that noticeable. Imagine a line of nine gigantic people, with one gnome among them.

And compare that line with a line of nine gnomes and one giant? In which line is the exception more notice-able? In row two. Giants simply stand out more than gnomes. Not because big is better, but because big is bigger: big takes up more space and so is more visible. So it's not strange that female crabs should fall for the male with the biggest claw. If they fell for the male with the smallest claw they would have to look for far too long.

Imagine a situation where you have to choose someone from a set of people. It doesn't matter for what. You can think of an arbitrary number below a hundred and choose the person who comes up with the right number. That's possible, and in that case you'll be making an arbitrary choice. You can also choose the person who gives you most money. Not that you want to make a lot of money for its own sake, but so that you can make a choice: there will only be one person who will be most free with his wallet. On the other hand, choosing the person who gives you least money is not very helpful. In that case everyone will simply give you nothing, and you still won't be able to make a choice.

I know a famous millionaire who is much in demand as a speaker. Every day he gets requests to appear some-where and until some time ago just dealing with all those requests took up a dreadful amount of time: 'Is it an interesting subject?' 'Is it far?' 'Are they nice people?'

Those were the kinds of questions he asked himself in weighing up whether or not accept the invitation.

Nowadays he does it a lot more simply: he goes to the group that pays most. Not that he needs the money: he's a millionaire and money means nothing to him, but based on this simple criterion he can decide easily and quickly. Even if you're a millionaire and don't care a fig for money, you can still choose the one who gives you most, but you can't choose the person who gives you least.

☞ Female crabs choose the male with the biggest claw because choosing the male with the smallest claw doesn't work. But they could also have gone for the male with the biggest eyes or the biggest yellow whatsit on his forehead.
☞ They couldn't have chosen the male with the smallest claw or the smallest yellow whatsit. Choosing big works, choosing small doesn't. But that doesn't mean in any way that big is really any good to you, or that big is better than small.

But why do those female crabs choose the male with the biggest claw in the first place? Why don't they choose the longest back legs or the male with the biggest red patch on his head?

The easiest answer is chance. Those females have to

choose on the basis of something, and choosing on the basis of a smaller claw doesn't work. So why not a big claw then? You might as well. But it's more probable that once – long ago when the fiddler crab claw wasn't nearly as big – a slightly bigger claw was of some use to the owner of that claw, or the female that chose the owner in question. Perhaps with a slightly bigger claw you could cut things better or something. A big claw meant 'good' and so the females chose those kinds of males. 'Bigger' meant 'better' and so the claw grew bigger and bigger; so big in fact that it was nothing but trouble. But well, by that time the fiddler crabs were already trapped.

Even more interesting is the fact that in the course of time such a big claw automatically comes to mean 'good', becomes a kind of hallmark.

In the first instance female crabs aren't at all interested in males with big claws; they want quality. But what has quality got to do with a big claw? Why should the male with the biggest claw be the best male?

Well, if all fiddler crab males do their best to acquire as big a claw as possible, and not all of them succeed, there must be something special about the fiddler crab male who does succeed. He obviously has qualities that the other males lack. He's the best fiddler crab!

It's just the same as with those ridiculous towers in San Gimigniano. The higher the tower the greater the prestige. That's nonsense of course: what good is a high tower to anyone? Why should the family with the highest tower be able to secure the best deals and the best jobs? Well, if all the families in San Gimigniano do their level best to build as high a tower as possible, there must be something very special about the family that builds the highest one. If in medieval San Gimigniano I had had to select a family to grant something to – a commission or a post or something – and I knew that every family was doing its level best to build as high a tower as possible, I would have granted the commission – or the post – to the family with highest tower of all, since they were obviously a family with a lot going for them.

If that family were the only one building high towers, though, such a tower wouldn't have meant a thing. In that case the family would simply be mad: 'They're a really odd lot, building a high tower. They think it's good for their image, but we know better. In the rest of the town we put the largest yellow globes we can in our front gardens, or wear diamond necklaces. That's what we call enhancing our image.'

The fact that such a high tower in San Gimigniano enhances one's image is a self-fulfilling prophecy: if everyone thinks there's something special about the highest tower, and if everyone tries to build the highest tower, then there's bound to be something special about the person who finally succeeds in doing it. What began as a useful storage space – which those towers once were – grew into a gigantic self-fulfilling prophecy. You see that frequently: some feature or other that in the first instance is perfectly useful develops in the course of time to absurd proportions. Something similar happened with Rolex, that expensive make of watch.

A new Rolex costs more than 15 thousand euros. Once they were mainly very good watches: hand-made, using the best materials – gold and diamonds – and they never lost a second. But step by step they got more and more expensive and more and more exclusive until they became what they are today: mainly expensive and exclusive, and their quality ceased to matter very much.

Rolex is so expensive because it's so exclusive. If you really want something special, you have to buy a Rolex. So why is it so expensive? Because it's so exclusive. Another self-fulfilling prophecy: you say that something is very expensive and exclusive and it automatically becomes true. Anyone can do it: if the fish and chip shop round the corner proclaims that its chips are terribly exclusive and special and so cost a thousand euros a portion, then it must be true. The average customer will be astonished and go on to the next fish and chip shop. As a result of which the chips will become even more exclusive, but it's not good business.

If you want to earn money from an expensive and exclusive product, it's sensible to begin with a good product, before going on to transform it stealthily into something that is mainly expensive and exclusive.

'Look, I really don't agree,' people have sometimes objected. 'Rolex watches are the best there are. They never lose time and they carry a lifetime guarantee.'

That may well be true, yet there are replicas that are also of terrific quality and that never lose a second. Even experts sometimes can't tell the difference between a genuine Rolex and a fake Rolex that is a tenth of the price or less. I don't think it's quality that makes the price so high. It's something else.

☞ It begins with something that's good or useful, and it ends with a self-fulfilling prophecy. That's the story of Rolex, the towers of San Gimigniano and the fiddler crab claw.

And so why do I find this so interesting? Because the statement 'The person with the highest tower is the greatest' is a self-fulfilling prophecy, but the statement 'The person with the smallest tower is the greatest' is not. If everyone were to think that the person with the smallest tower were the greatest, and if everyone tried to build as small a tower as possible, then everyone would have a very small, invisible tower. Everyone would be the greatest – or no one, that is. Which renders the initial idea 'The person with the smallest tower is the greatest' untrue. That idea is not a self-fulfilling prophecy.

Again it's all to do with 'being good at surviving' versus 'being good'. The idea 'big is great' survives more easily than the idea 'small is great', though both ideas are equally true in themselves. That's curious, isn't it? An idea that is neither true nor untrue, but survives more easily than its opposite – which brings me to the next topic, or question: are there other ideas? Ideas that survive better than other ideas, but apart from that are no better.

8

Why is it I think what I think?

We've seen a number of examples of things that survive, though we cannot answer the question 'Is it good that precisely these things should survive?' with a whole-hearted 'yes'. The fact that they survive is connected with the way the world happens to be made. Things that are not indestructible, are not maintained and cannot be copied are doomed to disappear, but they may be quite excellent things.

The question I want to ask is whether it's possible that we think things, or have beliefs, which as beliefs are good at surviving but for ourselves are less good to have. Is it possible that all of us should think X, though X is not true and it is not helpful to think X? Perhaps you find this an odd question but I'll ask it anyway: 'How on earth can that be possible? Thoughts that are good at surviving? Surely I determine what I think for myself? Surely I'm not saddled with unhelpful thoughts?

Surely I can't be the victim of the things I myself think?'

To be honest, I'm not that inclined to feel like a victim. I'm only a victim when something befalls me that I can do nothing about: when I'm run over or mugged. You could call one of those fiddler crabs a victim – of processes in nature, although victim is something of an exaggeration; the creature is not that bothered by the big claw and furthermore it knows no better. However, a crab with one of those big claws that keeps falling on its side really can be called a victim, I think.

Or imagine that my duck – the duck that broods for four weeks and loses weight – loses weight so drastically that she becomes ill, then we call her a victim too, a victim of her instinct, nature, genes or what have you. We view John & Annie as victims too, of their gullibility – that John & Annie who bought such a big fridge and provided the title of this book.

Ducks, fiddler crabs and John & Annie can be victims because they can't do much about the fate that befalls them. Whereas we, when we do something ourselves, seldom have the feeling of being victims. When I write a book and have sleepless nights when it's not going so well – as sometimes happens to me – I don't see myself as a victim. It's my own stupid fault. At most you could say that I'm the victim of my desire to write books. But even then it's still my own desire. And if a neighbour starts an evening class in business administration in order to get an even better job (he already has a pretty good one), we don't see him as a victim either. On the contrary: we see him as someone who's taking control of his own life.

Actually it's pretty arrogant of us, finding it easier to call ducks, crabs and John & Annie victims than ourselves. As if we are masters of what we do and think. But is that true? Why is it that we think what we think?

You're probably thinking all sorts of things, perhaps you're thinking of the garden that has to be dug, or of the next page, but those are not the kinds of thoughts that I want to discuss. I want to discuss the rather less fleeting thoughts, thoughts that last a little longer. Actually I think 'notions' is a nicer word, or 'ideas' or 'beliefs'. I use all those words fairly interchangeably, but always mean the same thing: 'something in our head'. Something in our head that leads us to perform certain acts and make certain choices. I have all kinds of notions too. For example I think everyone should be given equal opportunities. That idea is in my head. But there are many more of those kinds of things in my head:

You must work for your money.
Houses are usually made of stone.
Rabbits have floppy ears.
It's better to drive on the right in most of Europe.
George Best played football for Manchester United.
George Best was the best British footballer ever.
It must be terrific to be able to play football as well
    as George Best.
Soup is never a dessert.
You can't eat insects.
Prawns, on the other hand…
A secretary earns less than a manager.
It's nice to earn more.
You've got to make something of your life.
It's best if you make a detour when you see a bunch
    of Hell's Angels in a fight.
Jeans are blue.
Jeans look good.
Jeans are in.

All that is in my head. Not that you can find the above
sentences literally recorded anywhere: even with the
most powerful brain scanner you won't find the sentence
'Jeans look good' anywhere. But there's something in my
head that has to do with jeans and that leads me to buy
jeans instead of corduroy gardening trousers – which I
used to buy. How do those things get into my head?

Why is it that I think the above things?

Sometimes the answer's easy: I think that jeans are blue because it's the truth. Jeans are quite simply blue, rabbits have floppy ears and George Best played football for Manchester United. It's all true and that's why I think it.

But it's not true that it's better for me to make a detour when I see a bunch of Hell's Angels in a fight. At any rate it's a very different kind of truth from the truth that jeans are blue. Mainly it's helpful to think I should make a detour. Helpful to me. And that's why I think it.

There are still other ideas in my head, though, that are neither true nor helpful. How do those ideas get there? Why, for instance, do I think that everyone deserves equal opportunities? It's not true. In the sense that I can't go anywhere or something, to check whether everyone should have equal opportunities, as I *can* go to a clothes shop to check whether jeans are blue. Nor did I think it up by myself: that would be clever, but I'm not that clever.

I think it's to do with my upbringing. That my parents taught me that everyone should have equal opportunities. And probably they learned it in turn from *their* parents. I'm absolutely in favour of that idea about equal opportunities, and it feels as if it's my own idea, but I didn't think really it up by myself. I do certainly think things up now and then, but not terribly often. It's like using recipes: I choose them, but I seldom think them up.

Sometimes it's not clear whether I'm in control of my choices. I remember that a few years ago I was tremendously enthusiastic about the colour orange. I thought it was such a beautiful colour, and what a shame it was that there were so few orange trousers and orange T-shirts on sale. But just about at the same time my enthusiasm for orange began to grow, more and more orange trousers, jackets and t-shirts came onto the market. What luck; I could finally buy the clothes I wanted so much.

Now when I look in my wardrobe I don't know what got into me: 'How is that I ever wore these bright-orange trousers?' I wonder.

Did I decide for myself five years ago that orange would be my new favourite colour, or was I subtly influenced by pictures in magazines, shop windows and sporadic trendsetters in orange trousers? I'm afraid that it was to some extent the latter. There's nothing at all wrong with that, but it illustrates the fact that I felt I was developing my own personal taste, whereas I was being secretly influenced by the images around me.

Isn't it exactly the same with my notions? It feels as if I am master of the notions I have – just as I felt I was master of my own personal taste – but all things considered, I base my notions in large part on the notions of others around me.

My partner's family always arrive exactly on time for parties. They all come in together, and if anyone is running a little late – never more than five minutes – everyone waits for them for a moment. Round the corner from the party. That's the way to do it, in their opinion. But where I come from we do things very differently. Parties actually never begin at a particular time: people dribble in and leave again when they feel like it.

The difference between me and my parents-in-law,

when it comes to parties, has nothing to do with the air in my home town or other physical differences between two areas, but derives from the fact that we pick up ideas, beliefs, ways of thinking about things from other people. People around us, people we see or know.

The very existence of cultural similarities within regions, or within certain groups of people, illustrates the fact that the things we think are based on the things other people think — others in the neighbourhood, others we have contact with, others we learn about, etc. Not that I myself have no influence over what I think, but it still resembles choosing a recipe: I select it and seldom think it up for myself.

There is a kind of 'dynamic' in operation, a game, a process, a 'sequence of events', in which people adopt ideas from each other; one idea of Tom's, the other of Dick's and now and then something new is thought up: an economy of notions. Just as in the real economy there are products that float to the top and stay there for a while, so in the 'economy of notions' there are notions that do better than others and stay in our heads for longer.

What kind of notions are those? Notions that are good at surviving. And are they notions that are good for us to think?

9

Multiplication and division

We've seen that roughly speaking there are three ways of lasting a long time: 1) by being indestructible, 2) by being well maintained, or 3) by being copied often enough. This applies to everything: aircraft, hawk-moths and megaliths, but does it also apply to notions? Do, for instance, notions exist, things that we think, that ensure that they are multiplied? Is such a thing possible?

An example that comes directly to mind is rabies – admittedly not a notion, but certainly something that can get into heads: rabies is a viral infection of the brain. If you suffer from it you go mad in the sense that you become aggressive and start biting other people. That is how rabies spreads. Biting, though, is a rare symptom in people, but still rabies is an example of something that gets into your head and multiplies by manipulating your behaviour.

Another example is the liver fluke. It can also get into heads, though not into ours. The liver fluke is a worm that lives in the intestines of sheep, in its thousands. The liver fluke lays its eggs in a sheep's intestines, tiny eggs that the sheep excretes and that end up in the grass. In the grass there are snails that eat the droppings and tiny liver fluke larvae from the eggs invade the snails. The larvae in turn gather into slime balls that the snails deposit in the grass – yes, it's quite a story. Those slime balls are the favourite food of the ant. Ants eat the slime balls and so the liver fluke larvae eventually wind up in an ant – about two per ant. Once established in an ant, the larvae make their way to the brain of their host. The larvae are that small, that is, small enough to fit into the brain of an ant. There they manipulate the brain of the ant in such a way that the latter has the strange urge to climb as high as possible up blades of grass. Instead of going home like a well-behaved ant it does its utmost to reach the very top of blades of grass. Only to be eaten by a sheep… And the wheel has come full circle: the larvae grow into adult liver flukes in the sheep's intestines and so on and so on.

Ants can go 'mad' as a result of tiny creatures in their heads. Those tiny creatures multiply by using ants for their own ends. Tough luck on the ants, since they get eaten. Once again, we can't be affected by the liver fluke, but it is a nice example of how 'something in the head' can survive by multiplying at the expense of the owner of that same head.

Of course it could be done much more subtly. Imagine that I had a brain infection that made me suddenly like pop concerts or crowded football stadiums. Such an infection could very easily spread: the more people, the more chance of transmission. Except that such infections don't exist. And I can't immediately think of notions or thoughts that influence my behaviour to such an extent that more such notions are created. But they could exist, I think, and as notions they would be fantastic survivors.

Just imagine that I thought I had to proclaim the message on the radio. And that message is that everyone should proclaim the message on the radio.

'People, people, make sure you try to get on the radio in order to proclaim this message. So that there will be more people who know the message and that it is proclaimed as much as possible.' I don't think it would work. The listeners would shrug their shoulders and laugh me out of court: the story is too flimsy.

I'm reminded of a course that a friend of mine called Rudolf took a few years back, a 'life-improvement course' run by Landmark. With the aim of achieving a really successful life. Rudolf spent three days improving his life, together with a hundred or so other participants. And oh, he was so proud of himself. In a large auditorium he stood on a stage with hundreds of other people, weeping with happiness: 'I shall never, never, never be mean to my father again; I'll take him in my arms and tell him I love him!'

I know all this because I went with him on one occasion. That was part of the course: Rudolf had to share his progress with the people who were dear to him. As many friends as possible must experience his improvements so that everything could go even better. And like a good friend I went along for one evening.

I had a green badge pinned on me – for guests. Participants had a red badge and the facilitators were blue. Those facilitators, as it happened, were in turn also participants, but in another, much more expensive course. I was constantly cornered by these reds and blues: 'Great you're here. Whose guest are you? Can I invite you some time too?' At the end of the evening Rudolf also asked whether I would consider joining. And, goodness me, it was as if the success of his course partly depended on the number of new participants he was able to recruit. He didn't put it like that, and probably he wasn't that aware of it, but it was clear that he was keen for me to enrol. For me? For himself? For Landmark? Anyway, the course was far too expensive for me – 900 euros for three days – so I wasn't tempted for a moment.

But it was a cunning ploy. Rudolf really believed

that it would be good if more people took the Landmark 'life improvement course'. And what do you learn on that course? A lot, I'm sure, but also that it would be good if more people took a Landmark life improvement course. Surely, it seems to me, this is an example of a notion that manages to multiply secretly.

Well, that notion wasn't terrifically successful in this case: only three friends of Rudolf's finally succumbed. But there again, that's not that few. Thousands of people have meanwhile paid 900 euros, and that's only the beginning. For another 700 euros you can take the advanced course; and for 2,000 euros the 'master course', after which you are 'qualified' to do voluntary work for Landmark. Worldwide, approximately 150,000 people take part annually. Landmark has branches in over twenty countries – quite an achievement for Jack Rosenberg, a second-hand car salesman from Pennsylvania, and the founder of Landmark.

Perhaps it wasn't even malice aforethought on Jack Rosenberg's part, and he really thinks that it's good for participants in a life-improvement course to recruit new participants; but this aspect of his course – this multiplication aspect – has undoubtedly contributed to his success.

Rudolf really believed that it was important to recruit new participants. He no longer believes that. He's honest about it: Landmark has left something of an unpleasant aftertaste. But what would have happened if the course had lasted longer, or were still continuing, and if all Rudolf's friends had joined? Would Rudolf still have had that aftertaste? I suspect not. I suspect that Rudolf would be continuously improving his life happily and contentedly and would still be recruiting more and more new participants.

To be honest, I think there are such Landmarks, Landmarks that continue without interruption, and with huge numbers of participants. Christianity, for example, or Islam – both Super-Landmarks.

Where Landmark has fifty branches in twenty countries, there are thousands of churches and mosques in every country. Even the world's smallest country, Niue in the Pacific, with less than 800 inhabitants, has no less than fourteen churches. And those churches and mosques are not just offices, they're the most eye-catching offices that exist, and on top of that make a din twice a day. Amazing that it's allowed… Even the little village where I live, with a hundred houses, has a church, a gigantic building visible from miles away, like all the other churches around us. If there is one club that manages to multiply its ideology with fantastic efficiency, it is religion – Christianity and Islam. Landmark can learn a thing or two from them.

Furthermore, the religious really believe, as Rudolf

once did, that it's good and important to recruit new members. They think not only: 'Oh, how glad I am that I've seen the light', but they also think: 'And it'll be absolutely fantastic when others can also bask in that light.' To this end they employ whole broadcasting stations, magazines and newspapers. Some travel the world, specially to proclaim the good news.

I did not have a religious upbringing and I've never thought much of religions. But when I was about eight I went to church with my classmates, as they were taking their first communion, and I must say I was impressed. What a big building, what loud music – and all those eye-catching clothes. What infectious grandeur! Non-believers had nothing like this.

Modest faiths disappear. A faith that says 'Well, you could believe this, but it's not certain. Doubt to your heart's content, and what others believe might be interesting too. Don't go around flaunting your faith, just keep it to yourself' – that kind of faith dissolves, at any rate sooner than a faith that trumpets: 'This is the truth; proclaim it.' That doesn't mean, though, that the second faith is 'truer' than the first, or better to believe in.

There are probably all sorts of reasons why so many people are Christians or Muslims. Perhaps it's useful to be religious, it feels good, or it keeps you healthy. Or perhaps religious people support each other more than non-religious ones. But I have no doubt that one of the reasons behind the success of religion is that the faith multiplies, and multipliers are stayers.

I on the contrary feel an affinity with the things that do not multiply, which can be very beautiful things. There was once even a magazine specialising in this type of beauty: *The Clean Handkerchief*, a clandestine Dutch magazine that appeared regularly from 1941 to 1944, each time with a circulation of one. The magazine was extremely bad at multiplying, though apparently it was a very good magazine.

Years ago I once saw a pavement artist who was doing a chalk drawing – in the street, that is. Not a replica of some famous work, but an original drawing; and not in a tourist area with all kinds of passers-by, but in a godforsaken little square in a new town. (I'd lost my way.) With intense concentration he was putting the final touches to his work and I stood and watched him for a while. He didn't mind, but he obviously hadn't counted on spectators.

Then it started raining, quite hard. The drawing threatened slowly to wash away. 'Put something over it,' I shouted to the artist, and I rummaged in my briefcase for something he could use. 'Or take a photo quickly!'

'But it was finished, wasn't it?' said the artist looking up. 'And furthermore I had a wonderful time doing it. It was a great morning I thought it was a beautiful drawing. It really won't be any less beautiful for no one having seen it.'

He had a point there, but it took me a while to get used to it. For goodness sake, he'd worked on it all morning. For nothing! I consoled myself with the thought that I could remember the drawing – more or less, and if not, the artist could. But he contradicted me again. 'You must be daft, I can't remember all that. By tomorrow I'll have forgotten what I drew today.'

It felt unsatisfactory. I had the feeling that beautiful things should be preserved. Perhaps my reaction was a little over the top – the drawing wasn't all that beautiful – but really beautiful things should be preserved. In our opinion.

We want *The Night Watch*, or the Beatles' songs, or tigers to be preserved. What's more: we want to share *The Night Watch* with as many people as possible. So it's hanging in a museum, it's reproduced on postcards and posters. (Funny, though, that sharing and multiplying here mean the same thing: by sharing *The Night Watch* with as many people as possible the reproduction of *The Night Watch* multiplies.) If we were to treat *The Night Watch* like the pavement artist did his drawing, we'd be appalled. And we'd think it was a shame if the masterpiece were to waste languish for years in the basement of a museum. The thing must be seen, surely?

Beautiful things must be preserved and shared with as many people as possible. And of course we consider that idea – that we should preserve beautiful things and share them with as many people as possible – a splendid one. If we'd found it a repulsive or bad idea, we couldn't have listened to it, and so we share that idea with as many people as possible. We don't do it consciously, by saying 'Listen up: you share beautiful things with as many people as possible; now pass this message on.' But we do stress that idea, precisely by preserving and sharing beautiful things.

For example, when you tell people about a nice

holiday, for example, you're actually telling them two things: you're telling them it was a nice holiday, and you're telling them it's worthwhile telling people about nice holidays. In a kind of schematic step–by–step plan:

1 You have the idea that it's worthwhile sharing nice things.
2 As result you tell people about nice things – and show people what they look or sound like.
3 Between the lines you also tell them it's worthwhile to share nice things.

Therefore you're implicitly trumpeting the idea that it's worthwhile sharing beautiful things. The idea multiplies. Perhaps after all at the end of the chapter, I have finally found an example of an idea I believe in, and together with many others, not so much because it's true, but because the idea multiplies.

The alternative idea of the artist in the new town doesn't have this effect at all. If he lets his painting wash away and doesn't show it to anyone, he's not telling us that it's OK for beautiful things to wash away. He's simply not telling us anything at all! There's nothing to see and nothing to hear. Perhaps that's why the artist's idea is so exceptional. But his idea – the idea that we don't need to preserve beautiful things at all – is also a pretty nice idea, I think.

☞ We must put beautiful things on show and say sensible things.

☞ Those are both ideas that multiply, while the following alternatives do not; but that doesn't make them any the less true:

☞ It's OK for beautiful things to wash away and it's sensible to be silent.

10

Truths that are true because everyone thinks they're true

If everyone says A, I want to know why it is that everyone says A.

JOHAN CRUIJFF, Dutch footballer, 1966

OK, we've seen examples of ideas that survive because they're multiplied, but there were various ways of surviving. Maintenance also works. I can't think offhand how an idea should be maintained or can maintain itself, but I do know of ideas that prove lastingly true and that once they've become true remain true almost by themselves, which is also a kind of maintenance.

We've already seen something similar: with the fiddler crabs. The majority of lady fiddler crabs cherished the belief that big claws are great, and the exceptions, like Mrs Crab, gradually disappeared from the stage – I take the literary licence of speaking of 'beliefs' among fiddler crabs. This belief, having once got a foot in the door, is unlikely to disappear.

In fact the idea 'You'd do best to choose the male with the biggest claw' is only true because all those lady fiddler crabs think it's true. That's curious. Do we have those kinds of beliefs too? Oh yes, we have them too.

What about the truth that it's special to shake hands with the queen? It's certainly true that such a handshake is special: there are very few people whose hands are shaken by the queen. But there even fewer people whose hands have been shaken by the lady next door. Yet that is less special. In some way the queen is more special than the lady next door. And that's true, the queen is so special, because we *all* think she's so special.

Of course it's also very special to be thought special by everyone, but that is the sum of the queen's specialness. She's a good horsewoman and likes dogs; but in that sense everyone's a bit special. (The lady next door cooks especially good sprouts.)

As long as we all believe that a handshake from the queen is special, that will be true. After all, she can't shake everyone's hand, so it's very special when she does shake your hand. She could have chosen someone else's hand, but she chose yours. (You lucky dog. Really special.) It's true that a handshake from the queen is very special, but only because we all think it's true.

The point about the queen's handshake is a funny kind of truth. It's certainly really true; it's not some kind of illusion, but it's a truth that could just as well have been untrue. If we'd all thought that only a handshake from the lady next door was truly special, that would have been the truth.

Funny, OK, but is it important too? Or awful? It's not really awful as long as it goes no further than the queen's handshake, but there are more insidious examples. For example, not long ago I had a scratch in the paintwork of my car repaired. It cost me 300 euros.

'So why have I got to have that scratch in the paintwork repaired?' I asked my garage: 'Is a scratch like that bad?'

'Well, sir, it won't make your car go any less fast and

these days cars no longer rust. But it'll depreciate, you see.' My car was worth 500 euros less with scratch than without. 'And it'll only cost you 300 euro to have the lot resprayed. That's money for nothing,'

Money for nothing seemed sensible so I had the scratch resprayed. But why exactly?

If no one were to repair a scratch like that, the value of my car wouldn't fall by 500 euros with a scratch: there would be tons of cars with scratches and no one would lose any sleep over it. It's only because everyone has those scratches repaired that a car with a scratch drops in value. It's only sensible to repair scratches in paintwork because everyone thinks it is. This truth, which is only true because everyone thinks it is, cost me 300 euros.

Another example are the Olympic Games. They're amazingly important, we think. The last Games cost over two billion euros – that is, after all income had been accounted for – but we thought it was money well spent. Once every four years half the world watches weight-lifting and dressage. That isn't something self-evident. It happens only rarely that millions of people stay up at night to see weightlifting, or the 400 metres freestyle. Try organising a swimming tournament and not a soul will turn up to watch it. The reason we attach so much importance to the Olympic Games is that we all attach so much importance to them. Everyone watches, and because everyone watches it's something important, and so everyone watches.

What do we make of these kinds of truths? And mainly what do we make of the people who deny these truths? People like Mrs Crab, who think differently from others – Mrs Crab from a couple of chapters back who was sensible enough to choose a male with a small claw. The people who say 'Oh, the queen's not really that special, is she?', the people who don't have the scratch in their paintwork fixed, the people who when others think A think B.

On the one hand the people who think A are simply

right: it *is* special to shake hands with the queen; and simply everyone watches the Olympic Games and so they're important. On the other hand I can't totally disagree with the people who think B either. The truths that they doubt could just as well have been untruths. If everyone had been glued to the box every four years to watch Sesame Street, it would have been mega-important, and let's be honest: how special is the queen's handshake really?

You can, though, detect truths that are true because everyone thinks they're true. Transpose the situation to somewhere completely different and see if the truth remains true. Put the queen in Nicaragua and see if the people treat her with the same deference as her subjects. The answer is no. They won't know who she is and although they'll think she's a well-mannered lady, they'll find a handshake of hers much less exciting than we do.

I once experienced something similar myself. Some friends of mine have Napapiri sweaters, perfectly ordinary sweaters that you could just as easily have found in a cut-price department store – nothing special. But they talked so pretentiously about the sweaters that I began to take notice. 'They probably have a special bond with those sweaters,' I thought, 'there's nothing special that I can see about the sweaters themselves.' Until at a certain moment I saw Napapiri clothes hanging in the window of an expensive designer store, next to the Hugo Boss and Dolce & Gabbana. 'Aha!' I said, as the penny dropped, 'Napapiri is a special brand.' I didn't know that before, so I couldn't know either that there was anything special about those sweaters. Their specialness resided in the fact that you had to know they were special.

☞ **If A is true because everyone thinks A is true, then are the exceptions who think B is true stupid?**

It sometimes happens to me that I think B whereas most other people think A. Recently, I was ill for a few days and had to fill in a form for my employers' medical officer – I work for a university. 'What is the reason for your incapacity for work?' was question one. 'The reason?' I wondered. 'As in motive, rationale, underlying idea?' 'What is the underlying idea behind your incapacity for work?' A ridiculous question, don't you agree? 'You'd better ask God,' was my first reaction.

Because 'reason' and 'cause' are commonly used interchangeably I simply read the question as 'What is the cause of your incapacity?' But I still didn't get it. 'The cause of my incapacity? I'm just ill.' However, just answering 'illness' struck me as strange: the medical officer already knew I was ill. After all, that was why I'd been sent the form.

Perhaps by 'incapacity for work' the medical officer simply meant the same as 'illness'. In that case I should read the question as follows: 'What is the cause of your illness?' Well, the cause of my illness? How should I know?... Perhaps I should have put a coat on or I drank too much. I finally simply put 'illness': 'The cause of my incapacity is illness.' The answer was perhaps not comprehensive, but I found it the most correct.

Later I was told by the medical officer that my response was ridiculous. 'Surely it's obvious that you were being asked about specific ailments?' I should have put 'high temperature', 'flu', or 'sore throat'. 'Surely anyone can understand that?' Anyone perhaps, but I can't.

That's odd. It's odd not being able to understand

something that everyone else does, but it's also odd that everyone understands the question in the same way, although it can be interpreted in different ways. How can it be that everyone thinks the same? As if everyone has the same aberration, the same madness, which, however, is no longer called madness. I'm the one who's mad. I, who think B while everyone else thinks A.

I remember something similar happened to me at primary school too. All my classmates understood what weeds were, but I couldn't. Stinging nettles were weeds, and so were thistles. My classmates talked about it as the distinction between herbs and weeds was just the same as the difference between deciduous and coniferous trees, but that couldn't be true, I thought. What in one case were weeds in another case could perfectly well be a herb? Surely stinging nettles were no longer weeds if you grew them for nettle soup?

My classmates didn't bother their heads about all this and nevertheless could talk to each other perfectly well about weeds. They knew in dealing with each other what they meant, but I didn't understand them. I was the odd man out. A bit crazy, when it came to weeds, though I had thought about it for longer than they had.

When I go into a restaurant or pub with my partner, a strange kind of musical chairs begins in our search for 'the right place'. I never know what place that is, but

Chantal has a sensitive nose for it. She walks slowly into the restaurant. Her movements become hesitant. She looks left, right and shuffles right through the restaurant on a course that for me is entirely unpredictable, until she has found the place. Sometimes at the window – 'The obvious place.' But at other times on the contrary not at the window but with a view of the kitchen. 'The obvious place.' I don't know what the right place looks like, nor do I know the way to that place. In order not to cramp Chantal's style I follow her cautiously at a distance of one or two metres, just as a detective follows his tracker dog when it's picked up a trail.

For me Chantal has a bee in her bonnet – about tables in restaurants, that is. I haven't a clue what goes on inside her and she seems not to be able to put it into words.

Oddly enough Inge – a good friend of Chantal's – knows exactly what the right place is. If the three of us chance to go out to eat somewhere they both enter the restaurant in the same hesitant way. With antennae that I don't have and don't understand they feel their way through the room in search of precisely the same thing. At the same moment they decide to go left or right, and as if it were obvious they both sit down at the same table. I, on my best behaviour, pull up a seat. I don't understand what's been going on in their heads, but they understand each other perfectly.

I sometimes daydream that there are many more people with exactly the same bee in their bonnet. They would know exactly what the best place in the restaurant is, all except me. That would be odd: for now I have the feeling that Chantal and Inge have an odd bee in their bonnet, albeit the same one, but if there are lots of people who have that bee in their bonnet, then I'll be the one with the odd bee in my bonnet. Then I'll become the one who can't put himself in other people's shoes, the odd man out, the one who's crazy.

*　　*　　*

So, truths that are true because everyone thinks they're true, are truths that are firmly established. They're unlikely to change overnight into an untruth. There will certainly come a time when we think a handshake of the queen's as special as the baker's, but it will take a while yet. Meanwhile those truths remain true.

Yet they're strange truths. They're not true in themselves, or at any rate they are true in a different way than the truth that stones fall downwards and jeans are blue. Furthermore, they could just as well not have been true.

This has been another example of something that is good at survival but is open to objection.

11

The Lonely Planet *for thoughts*

'When is this guy going to get round to success?' Yes, yes, you're right: in the next chapter. But I did say it would be a long detour. First an intermezzo. A rather odd, formal story perhaps, again about a statement that remains true once it has become true, a truth that in the first instance isn't true, but that – once it has become true – will remain true for years to come, a truth that is good at surviving, but is not in itself true.

What do you make of the following sentence:

'*Most Londoners believe this sentence is true.*'

It's rather a strange sentence in that it is mainly about itself, but that's not what I'm talking about at the moment. What concerns me is whether the sentence is true. Probably not. Scarcely any Londoners will have read this sentence; and if they have read it they won't think much of it. But *could* the sentence be true? Certainly: if we organised a referendum in which Londoners were asked for the opinion of the above sentence; and if in that referendum the majority of Londoners tick the box 'true', then the sentence will automatically become true.

Imagine that such a referendum is organised and that the results are splashed all over the newspapers: '63 per cent of Londoners believe this sentence is true!' Or to make it complicated: 'Most Londoners believe that the sentence "Most Londoners believe that this sentence is true" is true.'

But what will happen to the truth of the above sentence if we repeat the referendum a few times more? To start with a month or so later. Even more people with tick the 'true' box:

'Of course; I remember it well: the majority of people in London thought the sentence was true. It won't be any different now.' Or 'Last time I went for "untrue" but it turned out I was wrong; this month I'm going for the "true" box.' If we repeat the referendum, the above sentence will remain true. And if we repeat the referendum a few more times, not much will change. A large majority will continue to think that a large majority thinks the sentence is true.

The sentence 'Most Londoners think this sentence is true' may just as well be true as untrue. But the sentence is so constructed that once true it will remain true. The interesting thing is that the opposite of the above sentence doesn't have that quality at all. That sentence will not remain true or untrue for years to come; that sentence will wobble up and down between the two:

'A minority of Londoners think this sentence is true.'

There's no reason at all to give this sentence preference over the other – or vice-versa: perhaps the majority think the sentence is true, or perhaps a minority.

Imagine that this second sentence becomes the second sentence in the referendum. Again people in London will scratch their heads: 'What am I supposed to know something about this time?' If 63 per cent again tick the 'true' box then something like the following will appear in the newspaper: 'The majority think that only a minority think this.' I admit it's complicated and I don't think the newspapers will venture into this kind of vague complexity, but that's not relevant right now. In any case the majority are wrong: if 63 per cent believe that the minority think this, then those 63 per cent are wrong. And so the following month the results of the referendum will be different:

'Oh dear, I was wrong,' a number of people will think, 'a good 63 per cent of Londoners believe that the sentence is true. That's a majority, so the sentence is not true. I'm changing my opinion.' And if enough people do this the newspaper will publish the news that 'A minority believe that a minority believe this.' You realise where this is leading, because the third time the referendum is held – let's hope this kind of nonsense never happens – the minority will change back into a majority: 'That's right; last time it was a minority, so it'll probably be one this time too. I'm ticking the "true" box.'

The sentence 'The majority of Londoners think this

is true' is just as true or untrue as the sentence 'A minority of Londoners think this is true'. But that first sentence has the quality of remaining true if it is true, whereas the second sentence wobbles back and forth between true and untrue.

Obviously there are 'sentences about the world' – things you can say or think about the world – which, once true, automatically remain true. It's as if there exists for those sentences a kind of trap in which they are caught when it snaps shut. Once true, always true, for years to come. The funny thing is that such a trap does not exist for the opposite of those sentences.

'That sounds all well and good, but are there more of those kinds of sentences? And preferably reasonably important sentences that have something to do with my life. Sentences that I think are true, but that are actually only true because once, accidentally, they became true?'

Phew… that's a tricky one. To tell the truth, they're hard to find. Google. Google may be an example.

If you type a keyword into Google a list of pages appears in which the keyword appears classified in order of 'importance'. The more references there are to a page, the more important that page is. I check the top page as standard; it usually contains what I need. There's even a separate 'I feel lucky' button for this, which automatically opens the top page. If there's something usable on the top page, I look no further and am satis-fied. I myself will refer to the page in question so that the page will increase in 'importance' a little further. Therefore: once a page is high in Google's ranking order, it will remain so. An example of something that remains true once it has become true.

Some 'truths' have it in them to become true and others on the contrary have a problem with the opposite. In fact they become untrue by themselves although in the first instance they were definitely true.

You probably know the *Lonely Planet* series: the well-known guidebooks for backpackers and low-budget holiday-makers. If the *Lonely Planet* writes about a bar in Thailand that 'this spot is terrific. You'll find many kindred spirits there, the readers who so appreciate our guidebooks' – then you can bet your boots that it will indeed be teeming with *Lonely Planet* readers. So the *Lonely Planet* is writing the truth. But it's good to know why it is that it's the truth. Do all those people go to the Mai Thai Bar because it's such a terrific place? Or do they go there because it's in the guide?

I'm sure it's true that the Mai Thai Bar is a terrific bar where you'll find lots of kindred spirits. The ques-tion is why that is so. Has it something to do with the bar, or something to do with the way truths come into being? I fear the latter. The *Lonely Planet* could have said the same about any other bar and it would have been equally true.

Funnily enough the *Lonely Planet* cannot write the following: 'This bar is a wonderfully quiet spot, an oasis amid the hectic life outside, but so marvellous and honest.' They can write it, but it will immediately become untrue: in no time at all it will be full of *Lonely Planet*-readers.

Some truths 'survive' and other truths 'die out'. Not because one truth is truer than the other: it's just as true the Mai Thai Bar is nice, or may be even less true than the statement that the other bar is such a wonderful haven of peace. But one truth remains and the other truth disappears.

✳   ✳   ✳

Imagine that there is a kind of *Lonely Planet* for ideas, a guide in which we look up what we think. 'What shall I think today then? I could think 'like this' or 'like that'. You know what? I'll look it up in the *Lonely Planet.*' Then you'll find, you're bound to find, thoughts that are praised in the *Lonely Planet*, thoughts that many will share with you. They will be excellent thoughts, thoughts that have proved themselves. But certainly not always the best thoughts. Just as the *Lonely Planet* will certainly not lead you only to the best bars.

Well, we don't look up our ideas in a guidebook for ideas, but we don't think up what we think all by ourselves. We learn from others; follow role-models. We certainly think up things for ourselves now and then, but not that often. It's more a case of a very big *Lonely Planet* that is written by all of us and from which we draw inspiration for our own ideas. What might there be in such a *Lonely Planet?* And what could it *not* contain?

One thing that can definitely be in it is that it's such fun to help write the *Lonely Planet*. 'Do you know what's wonderful: helping to write this guidebook for ideas, I really get such pleasure from it.' 'Yes, you're right, it's the best thing there is.' You won't find the sentence 'Helping to write the *Lonely Planet* is a complete drag'. And if it is there, I don't believe it: the writer of the sentence obviously felt the need to contribute. So it can't be that much of a drag.

There is no *Lonely Planet* for ideas, but it is the case that we have ideas that others before us have already had. We learn from other ideas, select interesting ideas. And some ideas are simply not easily 'selectable'.

Imagine that one fine day I make an important discovery. I discover that it's terrific playing patience all day long – and having an undemanding job – and that nothing more is needed to lead a wonderful life. And imagine that I also discover that this is applies not only to me, but to everyone. For the first few weeks you get rather bored, but after about six weeks you want nothing more. Don't ask me how I might discover this; just imagine it.

What should I do in that case: play patience to my heart's content or proclaim my discovery so that other people too can start enjoying their new life? The second might be nice, but if I choose that people will have difficulty believing me: 'Yes, that's what that guy says, but just look at him working himself to the bone. On television, lecture tours and it seems he also writes books. I don't believe a word he's saying.'

By proclaiming my message I'm also proclaiming that it's worthwhile proclaiming messages instead of playing patience, so undermining my own message.

But what if I do heed my own discovery? If I choose action rather than words and stay resolutely at home? Then you'll never hear about my discovery. Then there'll be nothing for it but for you to discover the truth for yourself, amid a cacophony of messages that maintain the opposite. All the messages you hear are from people who find it worthwhile to send messages instead of playing patience.

The message that it's fun to do nothing but play patience is one than can scarcely be proclaimed. Perhaps that's why we so seldom hear it.

And apart from that it's of course simply not true. I haven't tried it, but I can't imagine being able to play patience for more than a few hours. There might, though, be a grain of truth in it. Perhaps it's true that a little more lazing about is actually pleasant. Or perhaps it's true that for a handful of exceptions a life of nothing but patience is wonderful. For those people I can only hope, hope that one fine day they discover their truth for themselves. No one can tell them; those who believe it are too lazy.

The idea that lazing about is wonderful might well be just as true as the idea that working hard is wonderful. Perhaps, I don't know. But one idea has it in itself to conquer the world and the other idea does not – though that doesn't mean that lazing about isn't fun.

12

Why do I want to get to the top?

The last chapter suggested that the idea 'Just lead a nice lazy life' is one with little 'power of survival'. It's also rather self-contradictory: if everyone thought a lazy life was great, no one would take the trouble anymore to tell others that they should live as lazily as possible.

Perhaps the opposite idea, though, is precisely one that is very capable of surviving, the idea that we must get the most out of life, be successful, get to the top. Perhaps that idea will multiply, or maintain itself in some other way.

I want to get to the top. But why? Why is it that I want that?

Once in my life I got to the top. Literally: to the top of the Galdhøppigen in Norway. It's the highest mountain (2469 metres) and quite easy to climb. Climb is actually overstating it: in fact you simply walk up. It takes a couple of hours and you need to be fairly fit, but you don't need any very special abilities to reach the top of the Galdhøppigen.

I set out early in the morning and after a few hours' toiling the top came in sight. 'So there it is,' I said, looking hopefully upwards. 'That's what all the effort was about. Just a few more hundred metres.' However, once I'd covered those few hundred metres and finally reached the top, it was all a bit of an anti-climax. Of course, I could see for miles. And the hot chocolate was wonderful. But still I had the sneaky feeling that somehow I'd been taken for a ride – or had taken myself for a ride. Slogging away for hours for a plastic cup of hot chocolate and a view that you get tired of in five minutes; something's not right. And then I had to go back down. 'Why did I want to come here?' I wondered. 'Why do I want to get to the top?'

A challenging question because I immediately wondered whether I should ask myself the figurative variant. I want to reach countless peaks in my life: I toil away to make the most of my career, and apart from that I definitely want to write special books. Will those peaks be as big a disappointment as the Galdhøppigen?

The most obvious reason for wanting to get to the top is that it's so beautiful there, but that didn't apply to me. I couldn't see anything special about the Galdhøppigen, and I'm not the only one who thinks so. There's so little of interest on the mountain that no one wanted to climb the thing – except for one Steinarr Sulheim who in 1850 was the first, and a handful of oddballs after him – until in 1970 it was discovered that the Galdhøppigen is the highest mountain in Norway. Why exactly it was only discovered in 1970 I don't know: perhaps what had up till then been the highest mountain – the Glittertind – had melted a bit, or incorrect measurements had been made in the past, but in any case since then thousands have ascended the Galdhøppigen every year. Only when it was discovered that it was the highest mountain in Norway did people start climbing it. Don't tell me that people climbed to the summit because of the nice view.

A second possible answer is 'I've got to do something, haven't I?' I've certainly got to do something, so why not go to the top? Yet that can't be the whole answer. If everyone does the things he/she does because they've 'got to do something', you'd have expected a bit more variation in the things that we do. You'd have expected that people would occasionally stroke the grass on the slopes of the Galdhøppigen. Why not? And you'd have expected people to run circuits round the foot of the mountain. Why not? But we don't do any of those things: we climb up. Not all of us, but I wasn't alone when I walked up the mountain. Whereas I would have been alone if I'd started stroking the grass. 'Why not?' is not a sufficient explanation.

To be honest, I still don't know exactly what so attracted me about that summit, but I wasn't concerned about the top itself – that much I do understand.

Perhaps it was to with the fact that the Galdhøppigen stands out fairly clearly, much more than the surrounding valleys. In the valley the peaks stand out, but at the top the valleys don't: at the top other peaks stand out. Perhaps that's why I was so keen to get to the top and was prepared to toil for hours to get there. The top is a clearly visible goal; easy to want to get to, but no nicer than the valley on that account.

Perhaps something similar applies to the figurative tops I try to reach. They're all clearly visible. Good writers are put on a pedestal and win prizes, their names get into magazines and are mentioned. Professors have striking black gowns and once a year walk in procession through the town centre – that's noticeable. And TV presenters are always visible: channel-hop and you'll find a TV presenter – all day long.

If there are clear role-models for me, they are writers, professors and TV presenters. Perhaps that's why I wanted to become all of those. But is it fun…?

☞ **Perhaps I want to get to the top because it stands out so beautifully. Just like those figurative peaks: writer, professor and TV presenter.**

Without role-models I wouldn't know where to begin. The first people I started copying were my parents – they're perhaps the most influential role-models I have. I talk like they do: if they had talked Chinese I would be doing the same now. And if they'd played golf instead of having an allotment, I would probably have done so too (I now have an allotment). It isn't that my parents taught me explicitly that allotments are nicer than golf, but they did set me an example. And it isn't that I copy my parents unthinkingly, but they definitely influenced the things I do because of their exemplary function in my life.

But my parents are of course not my only role-models. What about the six-million-dollar man? The six-million-dollar man is a superhero from my childhood fitted with electronic bells and whistles to the tune of six million dollars. With his bionic eyes he saw every last detail and with his steel muscles he could outrun a car. I wanted to do that too! In the afternoons we played 'six-million-dollar man' games and copied our hero's behaviour. These days I have other heroes and copy them more or less unconsciously.

What would I do without role-models? I certainly feel I'm my own man and set my own course, but that course is based on the course others pursued before me.

I chose my first job because it paid well. But I was a little dissatisfied: I was drifting a bit, didn't know which way to go and after a while went to a career adviser.

'Who are your role-models in the organisation?' she asked me.

'No one at all; there are no role-models there.'

'But then how are you supposed to know which way to go?' she asked in surprise. 'If no one shows you, how are you supposed to know what to do?' She was right: it's nice to be able to base yourself on what others have done before you instead of having to think up everything for yourself.

I can imagine that you find that emphasis on copying role-models quite exaggerated and speculative. You have a point: we don't only do things that we were shown previously and furthermore there are lots of different role-models. Surely we have to make our own choice? But let's turn things round: how many times have you done something without someone having once done it before you? Probably you can think of something, and perhaps you'll even be proud of it. 'Certainly, I once baked an apple pie using pears. Completely my own invention; without a model and without a recipe.' However, it's probably no accident that you're so proud of that. You're probably not all that original – and neither am I.

One last example to try to convince you that role-models play an important part in the choices we make and the things we do. When did you first want a CD player? My guess would be somewhere in the mid-1980s – if you were already around then. In any case just after the CD player came on the market. First there was the CD player, and only then did you want one. 'Yes, of course,' you may say, 'how can I want something that isn't there.' Exactly; that's exactly what I'm arguing: we want things that are already there; and we do things that are already being done. There's nothing wrong with that, but that's how it is. I'm not arguing that we're all stupid sheep mindlessly following other sheep; but I am arguing that we learn what directions we can take from other sheep.

☞ I follow role-models; without role-models I'd scarcely know where to begin.

Now I've some more new role-models to base myself on. I read about them in the daily and weekly press. People who live meaningful lives and are influential. 'The country's greatest scientists speak.' I should have been up there with them, I think. Where did I lose it? Or there's so-and-so, 'the best writer of our time' – my new six-million-dollar man.

If I ever take time to read my weekly properly I'm confronted with those role-models and I resolve to start leading a more meaningful life; also publish in important magazines and to undertake things that matter. But even as I read I also resolve something completely different: the opposite actually. 'I should do this more often, Bas,' I say to myself, 'just read quietly for a bit; take more time and pay a bit more attention to things.' It happens regularly that I resolve to do this – in vain, of course, for now.

Two very different resolutions. One tells me to take more time and rest, while the other on the contrary tells me to raise my game. The first resolution – for heaven's sake rest a bit more – comes from myself. There are few role-models to show me that resting is good. Of course it says so in magazines and Oprah Winfrey may say it, but none of the role-models I see ever rest, Oprah least of all, and if they ever do rest, I don't see them. I see Oprah all hyped-up when she's presenting her programme, and not when she's lying full-length on the sofa, exhausted from yet another season of TV.

One resolution comes from myself and the other seems to come from outside, as if it's being imposed on me. That's not really the case. There's no one who thinks it might be a nice idea to put that Bas Haring under pressure, but under the influence of the role-models around me I put myself under pressure.

Could things have been different? Could I have been surrounded by examples of people relaxing, or very mediocre people doing nothing special? Imagine that the weekly papers were full of articles about Fred Smith – the man who can't do anything special – Penny Brown from Reading, with her new Volkswagen Polo. Would you go on reading that weekly? Or imagine that the most mediocre and insignificant patience-player were to appear as guest on Oprah's TV show. What would that be like? And who should be a guest on Oprah's show? There are thousands of alternatives:

'So you came 17th in your village patience tournament?'

'That's right. It's wonderful coming 17th. But 18th would have been nice too. Or 8th. It doesn't really matter that much.'

'May I ask where your village is?'

'I'm from Cleator Moor, England. There are lots of people who play patience there. But there are also lots in Whitehaven, that's not far away, you know. Perhaps you should invite someone from Whitehaven some-time. Or from Distington, or Clifton. They're not far either. Actually you could invite everyone onto this programme.'

Oprah can't invite everyone onto her programme, and nor can anyone.

She has to make choices, and she can't help choosing people who are 'selectable'. She *may* invite the winner of the Cleator Moor patience tourna-ment – although that would have a drastic impact on viewing figures – but choosing the average patience player from the Whitehaven area won't do. There are too many of them. It's the same as with the story of the peacock's tail: peahens have to choose, and so they choose the peacock with the longest tail. Choosing the least noticeable tail won't do: it doesn't get noticed.

There seems to be a mechanism operating reminiscent of the mechanism underlying the fiddler crab's big claw. That was a sad mechanism — at any rate for the crabs. It gave them big awkward claws that sometimes actually made them fall over.

☞ Female crabs have to choose.

☞ Oprah Winfrey and the weekly press have to choose.

☞ Choosing the most unobtrusive male is not on, so they simply choose the male with the biggest claw.

☞ Choosing patience-players from the Whitehaven area is not on, so they choose winners and other special people.

☞ The male with the biggest claw has the most progeny, which in turn have those odd big claws.

☞ The role-models around us have most followers, because without role-models we wouldn't know where to begin.

☞ So the claw gets bigger and bigger without benefiting the crab much.

☞ So we try to be winners or special in some other way — without it necessarily benefiting us.

Perhaps that's why I'm dissatisfied with a life of nothing but patience or weeding the garden. I need more and feel spurred on to get the maximum out of myself, achieve still more success and move on to the next peak – because that's what my role-models do. Of course patience-players, weeders and TV viewers are simply not particularly high-profile role-models, but maybe they're a lot better off, and they're laughing up their sleeves at how stupid I am to allow myself to be stitched up by a mechanism that hasn't got my best interests at heart.

'Yes, but,' you may react, 'this is far too simplistic! Surely this isn't the reason why I do the things I do?! There are countless people on TV – and in the weekly press – that I'd never want to imitate in all my life. What's more, I'll decide what I do and why for myself! I'm not an imbecile!'

Of course, you're right. You're probably not an imbecile. Probably much more is involved than the above simple diagram – but I still think the diagram is true.

Of course tops can be really nice: at the literal top there's a wonderful view, and at the figurative top you hold the reins, you're independent of others and you get recognition. Tops definitely have a lot to offer, but that's not the reason why I – or you – want to get to them — there's something else involved. Tops simply advertise themselves better than valleys, and if peak and valley are equally nice I'll probably choose the peak, because it stands out more, and is *able* to stand out more. Choosing the valley is not on. Because where is the valley exactly? The valley is more or less everywhere. While the top is a single point, a single clear point. And a metre lower is no longer the top. It's an easy choice, an easy goal.

Furthermore, why should you gain recognition at the top? Edmund Hillary — the first conqueror of Mount Everest — was acclaimed as a hero. It must be wonderful to be treated like a hero, but the question is: why receive recognition there of all places? Why don't we receive recognition in the valley? Surely it can't be that difficult to organise? Why don't we spread the recognition around a little?

'Yes but... reaching the top is built into us.' That's a possible retort. We're simply constructed in such a way that we want to get to the top. It's our biology that makes us competitive and tells us that we want to be better than others, want to get to the top.

That's also true, I think. It's certainly in our nature to be competitive. How it gets in there, though, is another story, a story you can perfectly well think up for yourself since it is very similar to the story behind the crab claw. Yet I don't think it's the only story: migratory birds go south when it gets colder, it's part of the creatures' nature, they can't help it. Dogs have sex in the street: they just do it; it's just how they're made. But we don't try to reach the top 'because it's just how we're made'.

There are all kinds of things in our nature: skipping in the street, masturbating to our heart's content and eating lots of whipped cream. But we're not encouraged to do any of these by the media, advertising or lessons at school. On the contrary, our urges are reined back. We're told that whipped cream is unhealthy and that masturbation is fine – though not too often and not in public – while on the contrary a possible natural instinct for reaching the top is encouraged. We're encouraged to get the maximum out of ourselves. Just playing the trumpet isn't enough: no, we must play *good* trumpet. Better than the rest, the best even. We learn not to be satisfied with who we are; we learn to be ambitious.

It's most likely true that we are by nature competitive, want to reach tops and have successes, but that doesn't detract from the fact that we live in a world in which we're covertly encouraged to reach tops, without knowing exactly what we'll find up there.

A few years ago a member of the Dutch royal family, now deceased, publicly abandoned the wearing of a tie. The gesture could have meant all kinds of things, but according to some people the tie was a symbol of modern slavery. Well, I find slavery a rather odd term: for me it evokes images of men with whips and emaciated wretches who do nothing but work. I do agree, though, with the observation that something unpleasant is in store for white-collar workers in ties. All that competition, all that hard work, all that stress – is that really much fun?

The image of employees as slaves has been suggested often before. The employee, it is asserted, works himself or herself into the ground. And for whom? For the *eminence grise*: the capitalist tycoon chuckling behind the scenes. I don't know to what extent this was ever true, but it's no longer true, or at any rate it's true only to a very limited extent. Although I certainly move in capitalist circles, I rarely have the impression that I'm dealing with devious or oppressive manipulators.

Nevertheless, without the presence of oppressive capitalists we (or the late prince) still have the feeling that something is up. Something that isn't good for us – or for the tie-wearing employee. So who is it who's oppressing us?

The answer is that we do it ourselves. We let ourselves be hustled by all those successful role-models and before we know it we've become a successful role-model ourselves – and if things go slightly wrong an unfortunate example.

The managing director sat in his house weeping and 'enjoying' his success. 'I want a house like that,' thought the poor wretches as they cycled past. But no one thought 'I want to weep as bitterly as that': weeping is invisible and a massive house isn't.

There is no chuckling *éminence grise* who uses us for his own ends. Unless it's our thoughts themselves that use us for their own ends, but I think a more honest image is of us as components in an enduring mechanism, a mechanism that we ourselves maintain by being parts of it, but one that doesn't have our best interests at heart. There is no controller behind the mechanism, no one we can blame it on. Perhaps that's why it's so tricky recognising the mechanism. I haven't even got a good word for it. 'Mechanism' is the best I can do.

'You're absolutely right,' was a reaction I had a while ago to the above story. 'I know a young man who was sick of ties, consultancy and stress. He decided to help his brother – his mentally handicapped brother. And just look what he's achieved: a flourishing business that finds jobs for handicapped people. He now has twenty permanent staff.'

Well, that wasn't quite what I had in mind. It doesn't have to be as grand as that. On the contrary: otherwise it starts smacking of success. Just helping your handicapped brother, invisibly and on a small scale – I think that's nice enough, or rather, nice for that very reason.

I once spoke to a racing cyclist, a very good racing cyclist. He's not anymore, but he was. At the age of sixteen he won a silver medal at the Junior Olympics and it seems that for a few weeks he even headed the world rankings for junior cyclists. That makes you the best in the world for your age category. A fellow-cyclist (also very good) once said of him that 'he'll take Dutch cycling out of the doldrums.'

But he didn't. He didn't feel like it. With a contract for a professional team in his pocket – at the age of 17 – and a glorious future in prospect, he started to think that he'd prefer to work as a carer with handicapped people, or be a poet. The best cyclist in the world preferring to be a poet!

We find that hard to take: how can someone like

that waste his talents? It took him three years finally to opt for what he really preferred: caring for the handi-capped and writing poetry. He's not even a good poet, which makes it truly beautiful. For years he had the feeling of having to fight against expectations of success: 'I think I have more of a problem relinquishing success than achieving it.' Obviously we – or at any rate our cyclist – are caught in a mechanism in which we feel we are being spurred on to get the maximum out of ourselves. But my next question is: '*For whom?*' For whom is all that success necessary? Obviously not for the ex-cyclist himself.

The desire for success seems like a new kind of reli-gion, with the media as its church. Just as religion survives partly by proclaiming 'the good news', so the urge for success survives through its own advertising. We're surrounded by successful role-models – because we can scarcely be surrounded by unsuccessful role-models: posters on which we're told that we're only really somebody when we're successful and adverts that assume that just playing the piano isn't enough but that we have to do it successfully. If we ever achieve success then we in turn become a role-model – maybe we even appear on such a poster one day. It is one great continuing mechanism – but well, that was already implicit in the etymology of the word 'success'.

'Oh,' you may say, 'I just feel good about my success.'

What on earth are you going on about? For me success and happiness are more or less the same. Great, just you carry on like that, in search of more success. But if you are the odd exception who can feel great without success, count your blessings: perhaps you're the one to be envied most.

13

'Nothing' is hard to see

People do not notice non-events.
DOUGLAS HOFSTADTER
IN *METAMAGICAL THEMAS*

The top stands out. It's easy to aim for. Just as it's easy to aim for a 'pee-fly', one of those flies painted on the porcelain of urinals in Dutch restaurants and airports at which men can automatically direct their stream to avoid making a mess. The fly works because it stands out, grabs the attention. When I stand at one of those urinals I aim at the fly. In itself very odd: there is less fly than 'non-fly'. Why don't I pee above, below, left or right of the fly? Obviously it's easier for us to aim at clear, unambiguous, well-defined things than at vague 'nothingness'. (Sorry ladies, you don't have this experience, but I assume you can imagine what I'm talking about.)

If you cycle all day – take a turn through the fields, for pleasure – and a dog suddenly runs across the road and you just manage to avoid it and cycle on – you'll probably remember that dog better than the fields you were cycling through. One clear, sharply-defined moment like that stands out, although it lasts only a short time, and turns out not to be of the slightest importance. But then, incidents stand out more than 'non-incidents', events that are non-events.

Just as an incident stands out from the 'non-incidents'; the 'pee-fly' stands out from the white of the bowl, the top stands out above all the valleys, and the winner is distinct from all the losers; so the result stands out from the way towards it.

Results – like the pee-fly – are clear and well-defined, measurable even. Two halves of forty-five minutes each and the result is 1-0. That is much clearer than the course of the game. 'And then their left full-back made a cross-field run from their penalty box almost to the half-way line; the keeper could easily have played the ball to the full-back; but fortunately Wayne Rooney got himself in such a good position that the keeper could only throw the ball out.' You don't say that. It would take far too long. Longer than twice forty-five minutes. So what do you say? One-nil: a nice summary of a complex match.

Results are nice and short and countable. Company results: 3.4 million euros. SAT test result: 543 marks. And the result of months of training and staying on the wagon: a bronze medal. You can count results, but not the route to those results, since it is far too complicated, too ill-defined and too vague. But the fact that you can only count results doesn't mean that only results count.

I sometimes sail with a bunch of friends, although I actually can't stand sailing, particularly the jargon ('Jib, luff! 'Ready to go about! Lee ho!') and the serious faces my friends pull when they use it...

So as not to sail around aimlessly my friends always head towards something, some beacon or other. Usually it's a tall flagpole or a church tower. Of course we don't really need to go to that church. What's more, you can't even get there in a sailing boat — but a beacon makes for good sailing – so my friends say. Having got close to the church we sail round for a bit and then choose a different goal – not because we need to go there but because it helps us enjoy sailing.

A wise lesson: in sailing it's nice to aim for clear, concrete goals, not in order finally to arrive, but to travel hopefully. In my view that's often the case. We aim at concrete objectives, results, and that makes it look as if those results are what really matter. But the reason we aim for them is that we can't help it.

Perhaps it's a kind of handicap of ours. Just as I find it a handicap in myself that I aim automatically and unthinkingly at that stupid pee-fly. We have trouble doing anything but aim at the pee-fly, the top, the incident or the result. But that doesn't mean that they're what really matters.

We need goals in order to keep travelling hopefully. Most things we do, we do with a certain goal in mind. I write books, not just because I like it but for other reasons too – to earn money and tell you things. And when I take the train it's always with a certain goal: to arrive at my destination. My fellow-travellers, in the same compartment, probably have the same goal. They're most likely not on the train just for fun, but for some other reason, some goal or other.

We're professionals at recognising other people's

goals. Near a zebra crossing we immediately spot some-one's intention of crossing. And when someone presses a button, we know they're not doing so for the hell of it, but to turn the radio off, switch on the light or open the door.

But sometimes we go a little overboard in identi-fying goal-oriented behaviour. We say of the water in the Rhine that it's on its way to the sea, as if that were the final destination, the goal of the water. We find it difficult to accept that arbitrary developments in nature are arbitrary; we prefer nature to be on its way some-where.

Perhaps we exaggerate in the same way when we consider our lives. As if our lives were headed some-where. As if we live life for some reason, something other than life itself.

14

Heroes

I don't want to die at all; I want my name on a banner in big letters.

AN ANONYMOUS SUICIDE TERRORIST IN *EMOTICON* BY JESSICA DURLACHER

Some people are almost automatically a role-model. Without doing a thing, like firemen, for instance, with their macho black uniforms, impressive helmets and bright red fire engines. I wonder how many children have thought 'I want to be like that!' The whole image of the fire service constitutes one big role-model.

Other people are made into role-models, put on pedestals or given a hero's welcome at the airport. Such a person was the Dutchman Jan van Speijk (afterwards referred to as 'the naval hero'). I know him from the lighthouse named after him in a seaside town where we sometimes holidayed when I was a child. It was an archetypal lighthouse with red and white stripes, and at its base there used to be a fish stall where we sometimes bought herring. My father would look up thoughtfully and start talking about the naval hero. He always tells you things twenty times, and probably I'll have the same problem later – or I've already got it. 'He blew himself up for the country, my boy, in some war or other.'

Indeed he did: in 1831 blew up his own ship in Antwerp harbour, so that it shouldn't fall into the hands of the enemy – the Belgians. He blew up along with it and of course perished. The archetypal example of a hero: did something that wasn't good for him, but was good for others, in this case the Dutch.

I can understand our elevating this man to the status of hero by naming a lighthouse after him and giving his name to streets all over the country. We do that to thank him. I understand that, but I understand a lot less well the fact that there are still people who want to be as heroic as he was.

If someone gives me a thousand euros I thank that person profusely, of course. It's never happened to me, but I would certainly thank the generous giver. I'd send a bottle of champagne, or put them in the limelight in some other way. Perhaps I'd write a column or hang a photo of them in the toilet. That's understandable. It's understandable that you should thank someone who gives you a thousand euros. It's less understandable that you should give someone a thousand euros just like that.

As far as I'm concerned it's a bit like that with heroes. I can understand our thanking the naval hero – or William the Silent or Vincent van Gogh – by naming a lighthouse after him, but I find it less understandable that we would want to emulate the naval hero. What good does it do you? None at all, that's the point. Otherwise you wouldn't be a hero. Being a hero means precisely becoming something that is no good to you. I understand all of us wanting to thank heroes. I can't understand anyone wanting to be a hero.

'But absolutely no one wants that! No one wants to be a hero! And precisely because no one wants to be one, we thank the people who nevertheless became one.'

There's something in that. If you were to ask people whether they'd like to be a hero, they'd probably deny it, but I suspect that many would like to, in their heart of hearts.

Not so long ago there were elections for the greatest Dutch person of all time. William the Silent, Anne Frank, Vincent van Gogh were all wheeled out – and of course the great footballer Johan Cruijff. The fact that in ten years' time a new greatest Dutch person of all time will be chosen says something about the limited meaning of 'of all time', but that's just an aside.

A whole TV series was devoted to the vote, in which panels discussed the merits of great Dutch figures and Dutch celebrities argued the case for their particular hero, their greatest Dutch person, whom they defended fervently. It sometimes looked as if they themselves would secretly have liked to be such a great Dutch figure, and sometimes that question was actually put. 'But wouldn't you yourself have liked to live such an illustrious life?' And with a jealous twinkle in the eye most advocates admitted that that they would have liked to. One such person said that he was prepared to give up part of his life in exchange for the certainty of being elected greatest Dutch person in the future.

Odd, though, because those great Dutch figures weren't at all enviable. Their heroic deeds did them no good; that's precisely why they were heroes. William the Silent was assassinated, Anne Frank was obviously not enviable, and Vincent van Gogh didn't benefit in the least from having left us such a gigantic oeuvre. We benefit from it; he didn't.

I don't think that those advocates were odd exceptions. In my view many people would be absolutely delighted to live a life that would endure down the ages, a life on a grand scale, remembered by many people, perhaps even a street named after them...

But how could that come about? Why do we want such a thing? Perhaps because we're surrounded by heroes as role-models. Street names and statues are heroes, people who have had meaningful lives – not for themselves, but for us. It stands to reason that we should erect statues to those people. But surreptitiously and perhaps unconsciously we are recruiting tomorrow's heroes.

What is actually the idea behind statues, street names and other monuments in honour of great and important people? The revering of existing heroes, or the recruiting of new ones? And what would happen if the hero were thanked not by a large statue in the street, but by a vague comment on the side of a shoe box. 'Hey, you're a hero, but be sure not to tell anyone.' Then the hero would no longer be a role-model. Would we still want to be a hero?

I've certainly got my own heroes, whom I admire and respect, and whom if I had money I might even put on a plinth. But there is this slight air of 'employee of the month' clinging to the hero.

You can become 'employee of the month' if you work, for instance, at McDonald's – or at any rate you used to be able to. You work your socks off for a whole month and as a thank-you your photo is hung up in all the branches in your area. Obviously it's your photo and not someone else's, but the question is whether the 'reward' is worth the effort. Furthermore that photo has an infectious effect on your colleagues: 'I'd like to be up there too some day,' they think. Oddly enough. But it works – well enough. Otherwise McDonald's would have dropped 'employee of the month' long ago.

Would anyone want to become 'employee of the month' – and work so hard for it – if it were kept quiet? 'Hey pst… you've been made 'employee of the month'. Well done, lad, but don't shout it from the rooftops.' Fewer people, that's for sure.

Just as it is a mystery to me what possessed the naval hero, it has long been a mystery to biologists why there should be suicidal animals. Because they do exist: bees, for example.

They sacrifice themselves for 'the good of the hive': enemies that penetrate the hive are stung and the stinging bee usually dies as a result. Or some spiders: there are mother spiders that give themselves to their young to eat. How can such creatures exist, and particularly: how can they continue to exist? A sporadic kamikaze bee isn't that odd. But it's mysterious that there should be swarms of them: that kind of bee soon runs out, you'd think

Imagine that the Martians land on earth for the first time and quite by accident find themselves in the middle of a stock car race. You know: one of those races with battered old cars that do little else but slam into walls or each other. The situation is bound to be mysterious for the Martians: 'What are those strange beings doing?' they'll probably think: 'They're destroying each other.' The cars are displaying behaviour that is clumsy and destructive to themselves and any Martian worthy of the name understands that something odd is going on: 'How can these creatures exist? Creatures that systematically destroy each other surely become extinct in no time? They destroy themselves in the first place: that's the curious fact,' think the puzzled Martians. Until a driver gets out and the penny drops for the Martians. 'Aha, inside those creatures there's another creature, and presumably it's at the wheel.'

A stock car admittedly behaves clumsily for itself; it has little say in the matter. The man at the wheel (they're almost always men) determines what the stock car does and he is the one who benefits, wins prizes, enjoys himself or whatever. Furthermore, the following week he simply buys a new stock car.

Does something similar apply to us? Do we have drivers inside us that in fact hold the reins and sometimes cause us to do things that are bad for us but good for them? It doesn't feel like it; it feels as if I'm my own driver, and I don't get the impression that there's another mysterious driver inside me. Just as well.

Yet in some creatures there definitely are such drivers. And it's precisely these drivers that explain why it is that bees and spiders sacrifice themselves. At first sight that seems mysterious, as mysterious as the self-destructing stock cars: spiders that allow themselves to be eaten obvious have less chance of survival than spiders that do not. But those mother spiders can't help it. Their behaviour is to a large extent instinctive – such a creature has no influence over it – and that instinct is genetically determined. The genes of such a spider are as it were at the wheel.

They steer the spider in such a way that the spider sacrifices itself for its young. That's nice for the young: they have their next meal. The trick is that the same genes are in those young, since they have acquired them from their mother – and from their father.

The genes have the power and sacrifice mother, but in that way return with redoubled power in the next generation. They use their power to multiply at the expense of the poor mother, and to some extent also at the expense of the female young, since once they have become mothers they also allow themselves to be eaten.

In nature you see that quite often: that creatures behave unselfishly – perhaps sacrificing themselves – but that in fact, behind the scenes, a secret profiteer is pulling the strings.

The Dutch naval hero was an extreme kind of hero. A suicide-hero. Modern suicide-'terrorists' are actually latterday Dutch naval heroes. But there's a big difference: it took the Dutch naval hero more or less by surprise, whereas modern suicide bombers prepare for months for their 'task'. How is it possible that people should do something so stupid in a well-prepared and supposedly conscious way. Something so stupid for themselves.

There are many stories that (partly) explain this mystery, but one of those stories is that those suicides are honoured on a grand scale in demonstrations in which their names and photos are borne through the streets. Hundreds of people follow a banner carrying the name of the attacker and whole-page ads appear in the paper. 'In honour of the brave and courageous fighter whose name shall be remembered for all eternity.' They're treated like 'super-employees of the month': on the one hand to honour the heroes who gave their lives and on the other to recruit more new heroes.

'I don't want to die at all; I want my name on a

banner in big letters,' says a Palestinian girl training as a suicide 'terrorist'.

Just as the stock car driver steers as he thinks fit and spiders use spider mothers for their own ends, the message on the banner seems to control the behaviour of Palestinian girls. Who is here for whose benefit? Does the girl have the desire to lay down her life? Or does the desire possess the girl? Does the desire use the girl for its own ends? So that the girl sacrifices herself, her name is borne in pomp through the city, and in that way the same desire multiplies and is reinforced in other young girls?

It's unclear to me who has control of whom here, but whichever way you look at it, 'the girl has the desire to blow herself up' still sounds rather one-sided. The other way round sounds equally reasonable: 'The desire to be blown up has found another girl.'

That girl, though, wasn't at all stupid. Suicide-bombers are not more stupid than ordinary people. There are very sensible, well-educated people among them. That makes you think. If there are people who under the influence of banners and messages are prepared to lay down their lives, then isn't it logical to assume that there are very many people prepared to give up a small part of their lives as a result of the messages around them? And aren't we – you and I – that kind of person?

15

Can Manchester United rejoice?

Up to now I have given various examples of things that are good at survival, but which apart from that are open to various criticisms: genes that programme a spider to allow itself to be eaten survive, but are not good for the spider; and Sportlife also survives but is no better as chewing gum than PK. I've also given examples of things with a certain charm that nevertheless disappeared or were doomed to disappear: the intelligent Mrs Crab who went not for big but small crab claws; the anarchist group who refused to organise themselves; the inefficient local patissier; and the strange idea of the artist from the new town that it's perfectly OK for beautiful things to be washed away – and several other such things.

Now it's time consider a category of things that is special to me – and the question of its survival or otherwise: groups. Specifically groups of people: clubs, teams, organisations, societies.

I occasionally have the feeling that some groups survive, are victorious over other groups at the expense of their own members. I had that feeling for the first time in my student days when I rowed in a very successful rowing crew. The team won lots of medals, but the team members in fact lost: at a certain moment everyone had acquired injuries and none of the oarsmen who had started the season was left. In the next chapter I shall cover this curious period in my life at greater length, but first I'd like to consider the question whether a team, group or club can suffer, experience pleasure and whether it's so terrible if a group ceases to exist.

The student club and the anarchist group have disappeared. Not so much because they were bad societies but because they were set up in such a way that they could scarcely survive. Is that a disaster? Is it a disaster when such a club disappears?

It may seem like it. I know an ex-member of the student club who doesn't like the fact that his society no longer exists one bit. The fact that he no longer sees his friends is all well and good; but the fact that the club is no longer there pains him deeply. Remarkable, really, because if all the friends accept it, who could consider it a terrible thing that the club no longer exists? The club itself? Can it have an opinion then?

Ten people can be peeved at the same time; but I

don't think a group as a whole can be. If I'm peeved, my neighbour is, and you are too, then the three of us are separately peeved, not collectively extremely peeved. Being peeved is in my view not a quality a group can have, and nor is being glad.

A group can do all kinds of things that members of groups cannot: divide itself in two, for instance. An individual can't do that – or walk in a line. Ten people can, but one person can't. Conversely, individuals can do things that groups cannot. Give a pass: one footballer can, but a team can't. You don't say 'the team put through a lovely pass', you say that David Beckham put through a lovely pass. On the other hand you do say that 'the whole team is over the moon'. Evidently a team can be over the moon, though I think it's a marginal case. If eleven footballers are over the moon, is a team a very long way over the moon? In my view experiencing pleasure is really something a team cannot do.

To be able to do that, you have to be put together in a quite complicated way. We can experience pleasure because our brain is so constructed that it enables us to do so, but if eleven individual players can experience pleasure it still doesn't mean that a team as a whole can do so.

It's not at all odd that a group cannot do things or does not have things that the members of the group can do or do have. A tree has a bark, but a wood doesn't. One euro can roll, but a pile of coins cannot. A thread is fragile, but a sweater is not.

I regularly get this wrong; I act as if a group has all kinds of qualities that a group can't really have. When I was small, the stork was threatened with extinction in my country: more intensive farming meant there was less for them to eat and they flew into power cables – a dreadful sight. Many people were concerned about the future of the stork, and so was I. Would there be any storks left in this country in a little while? That was the fear, more or less. However, thanks to a breeding programme since the 1970s the population steadily increased. Today the stork population is about the same as it used to be. A happy outcome!

But why happy? And especially: happy for whom? Happy for me because I like seeing storks in flight – but the storks that once flew into power cables won't come back. They don't benefit from the restoration of the population; and nor does the population – in the sense that the population isn't, for example, delighted that it's back up to strength. Populations have absolutely no opinions at all, and so they don't mind shrinking either or eventually dying out.

So would it be terrible if the stork as a species became extinct? Well, I wouldn't like it, but the stork population couldn't care less: species don't have opinions. Furthermore the storks themselves don't care much either. They don't give much thought to the survival of the species. They don't even know what a species is. Of course it's a shame for the last stork: it will probably feel lonely, but that's about it.

'Yes, but hold on. If the extinction of a whole species isn't terrible, then what on earth is terrible?'

Pain. I think that's terrible. And grief. Pain catches me unawares when I hit my fingers with a hammer. I can't do anything about it and however hard I try, the pain doesn't get any better. I can't change the pain into something good, something that feels nice or anything else that's positive. I can't do anything but resign myself to the fact that my body is so constructed that it can suffer pain, and pain is a terrible thing.

Groups don't suffer pain or grief. At least as far as I can see. When Chelsea lose, I see eleven players who are all sick as a parrot; but not one team that is as sick as a parrot. And if low-lying areas are flooded, those areas feel no pain, though the inhabitants do.

I find it difficult to empathise with a group. I can empathise with separate individuals, but I'm not really sure what 'the interest of the group' is. Yet we talk about it very glibly: 'the interest of the group'. As if we know what it is.

The interest of a football team – to return to that for a moment – is something different from the sum of the interest of the eleven individual players. 'In the interest of the team we have sacked all eleven players,' the Chelsea chairman might say. It may be a rather odd decision, but I can imagine a possible context. And if the team wins the premiership with eleven new players, then it will definitely have been in the interest of the team to sack the eleven previous players. But it wouldn't have been in the interest of those eleven footballers.

I understand more or less what the interests of an individual footballer are. He wants pleasure, money, wants to cruise around Barcelona and other such things. The interests of a whole team remain a little hazy for me. What does a team actually want?

It seems as if the interests of a group are more important than those of an individual. And I feel that too:

that's how I was brought up. The interests of ten others are greater than the interests of me on my own. It's nice when you enjoy something on your own; but it's even nicer when ten people enjoy. Pleasure times ten is better than pleasure times one.

But there is a difference between ten times the interest of an individual and one times the interest of group consisting of ten individuals. The former I understand, but the latter remains rather shadowy for me. I can identify with the individual interests of 16 million Dutch people; I know more or less what Dutch people enjoy and what is good and not good for them. But what is good for 'the Netherlands' I've no idea.

'Yes but, doesn't the Netherlands simply stand for all Dutch people? If something is good for the Netherlands, we mean good for all Dutch people – or most in any case.'

Yet I think it's a bit different. In my view the Netherlands means something other than all Dutch people, just as the Manchester United first team is something other than the sum of eleven individual players. Similarly, if something is in the interest of the United Kingdom, it is not automatically in the interest of all its citizens.

I had builders in from a former fishing village. My goodness, they work hard, those builders! They delivered five thousand kilos of reinforced concrete to our house, at the double. From the church square, over a bridge to our house – a distance of a hundred metres. At the double!

'Those villagers,' say my neighbours, 'it's their culture; they work so hard.' 'And it's got them a long way, you know,' my neighbours also say. 'They had to, didn't they? Otherwise they'd have been overshadowed by neighbouring villages.'

'If they hadn't worked so hard, some other village would have been number one today. Mark my words!'

Good for the village that the villagers work so hard; but is it also good for all the villagers? 'No, not exactly,' say the same neighbours again, 'they die early, from all that hard work. That's what you get, don't you...'

'Villagers like that don't last long. They're like a

racing car engine.'

Good for the village, but not good for the villagers. Such a thing is evidently possible. Of course it's only my neighbours who say so, but I find their story quite plausible. Obviously the interest of the village is something different from the interest of all the villagers.

It's a little like the story of Taiwan – the Asian counterpart of that Dutch village. Oh, oh, how hard those Taiwanese work. And oh, oh, how good that is, for Taiwan. But for the Taiwanese themselves? They're not that comfortable in their own skins, the least comfortable in the Western world, it seems. Good for Taiwan, but not good for the Taiwanese.

One last example illustrating that the interest of a group is something other than the sum of the interests of its members: the interest of the group of chickens bred for the table.

These chickens are very clumsy: it's no joke being one. Such chickens don't put up much resistance when they face slaughter. They're 'used' to it, not in the sense that they've been through it all before ('Oh, don't worry, they just chop your head off and after that you don't know much more about it'), but these chickens are bred for their 'docility'. Furthermore, they cook nice and quickly to make broth, and their feathers come out relatively easily, which is handy handy for plucking.

Very inconvenient for each individual chicken, but

convenient for the species. The group of chickens survives thanks to qualities that are particularly inconvenient for the individual chickens. That's possible, evidently. The interest of the group is evidently something different from the sum of the interest of its members.

☞ **A group can do things an individual cannot, and conversely an individual can do things a group cannot.**

☞ **An individual can experience pleasure and suffer pain, but a group cannot. At any rate not as a group: if eleven footballers are as sick as a parrot, that is eleven instances of being sick as a parrot and not one instance of being extremely sick.**

☞ **I think suffering pain is bad and I think 'being comfortable in your own skin' is good; those are my starting points. And of course I think it's nicer if eleven people are happy in their own skin than if only one is.**

But… the above leads to the necessary conclusion that I have a problem with groups that survive in a way that causes the members of the group to suffer pain or in a way that reduces their pleasure. The question is of course whether such groups exist. And if they exist, what am I to make of them? Or what should I do if I find I am part of such a group?

16

Winning teams

In my student days I rowed for a while in a 'coxed four': four oarsmen in a boat steered by a cox, travelling as fast as possible. That rowing was a serious business. We trained frequently (about four or five times a week as I recall), and once a week there was a race. We were a tightly-knit team; urged each other on, often ate together and helped each other study. I even remember the cox once missing an oral exam to help two team-mates with theirs: 'Two orals are more than one oral, so it only stands to reason I should help you two.'

'All for the team!' was the cry. I believed in that cry. The team meant a terrific amount to me and I was fanatically dedicated. I regularly rowed my heart out, to the point of throwing up. For the team: 'The Featherlight Boys'. That attitude was also the secret of our success. In other teams there were sometimes disputes and people thought about themselves. When that happens you don't row as hard. We thought of only one thing: each other. Marvellous, wasn't it?

In order to keep performing at a high level all season the team sometimes changed its composition. Then we rowed interim races with other members of the rowing club and the weaker members of our team were replaced by stronger oarsmen – if there were any. That's how it was. And it worked, because we won a stack of medals. With the new members we continued on the same footing: eating together, being a tightly-knit unit and training hard. The cry was still: 'All for the team.'

The first time I began to wonder exactly what we meant by that cry was when we were in a race against an ex-team-mate – Peter. Peter had been dropped a few weeks before and had found a new boat. Of course not such a good boat and we won the race, but I began to wonder whose interest that team interest actually was. The interest of the team was evidently something different from the interest of its members, because we threw the latter out when they no longer came up to scratch.

The same fate eventually awaited me. I'd trained so hard and thrown up so many times that at a certain moment I couldn't go on; I was replaced by someone else, in the interest of the team. A very successful team: no team won as often as ours that year. But exactly who or what that team was, was not that clear. At the end of the year none of the original crew was left. Every member of the team had been replaced.

Later I asked some ex-team members what they thought about it. Including Peter:

' I think it makes perfect sense. That rotation is good for the team,' said Peter.

'But who is that team then? I'm not in it any more, and nor are you.'

'But surely it's nice for the team when it wins?'

Nice? If you ask me, teams don't find anything at all nice. And four people can find something nice four times; but if you ask me, a team of four people doesn't find anything at all nice. A rowing team doesn't find it nice to win or terrible to lose at all. Individual oarsmen have opinions.

I don't know who I rowed so hard for, but it wasn't for myself – I'm left with a serious injury from all that hard rowing. And nor was it for my team-mates. They also rowed to the point of vomiting, and some gave up altogether after they had been thrown off the team. It looks as if I rowed my heart out for some vague group or other: a team. A winning team, that's true. And I contributed to the success of that team; but who or what profited from it isn't so clear. At any rate the team members didn't. They all dropped out – injured or not.

It was as if The Featherlight Boys had taken on a life

of its own – as if it had really become someone. And instead of feeling involved with each other as team members we felt involved with the team. Not that the team liked that. Teams have no opinions at all. But the team certainly won. The Featherlight Boys.

☞ I rowed my heart out for the team.

☞ Partly as a result the team won so many medals.

☞ But at a certain point I was dropped, like all my other team-mates.

☞ Who had finally won – the team, or the team-mates?

☞ It looks as if the team was the winner. But what's the good of that? Teams don't enjoy their victory; teams can't do that.

What should I have done? Should I really have gone on rowing till I threw up? For the greater good? So that the team won? Or could I have taken it a bit easier? In that case The Featherlight Boys would have won less: teams in which people take it easy don't win. But for the members of the team it might have been a lot more pleasant: no more throwing up and definitely fewer injuries too. Opting for the team seems to be opting for the greater good. But it might have been better if I had opted not for the team but for my team-mates.

I can imagine your finding this an odd story: 'People don't go through fire for a team; people go through fire for team-mates.' But I don't really believe in that. Or at any rate I don't believe that's the only thing. Of course I felt involved with my team-mates: Bert, the cox, who weighed no more than 50 kilos and yet could shout like a bear weighing 100; and Jimmy, the stroke. I definitely felt involved with real people; but I also felt involved with the team, a vague grouping that survived, even without Bert and without Jimmy. And to be honest I rather regret that: I prefer to opt for people rather than for the common denominators under which we group them.

The teams that win are the teams whose members commit themselves to the team to the point of throwing up. But I continue to find it puzzling what all that commitment is necessary for. The team may win; the members of the team have to throw up. Furthermore a team doesn't enjoy the victory at all and the team-members are upset by that throwing up.

It may be I'm presenting this in a slightly black-and-white way. As if doing your best for your team is something quite different from doing your best for your team-mates, and as if the consequence of that is that you'd be better advised not to do your best for the team. However, I don't want to put it in such black-and-white terms at all. I do want to maintain that the way I've presented it is also true. If you opt for the team – the greater good – you are opting for each other: your team-mates, your mates. You support each other and you care about each other. That's wonderful, but incidentally, and without it always being clear, you're also perhaps opting slightly for the idea 'team' – the name of the team, the history, the fame – and I don't really understand opting for *that* greater good.

☞ **The interest of the team is different from the sum of the interests of the members.**
☞ **Its perfectly possible for the team to win while the team-members lose.**
☞ **When you find yourself in such a team, I find it difficult to understand why you should opt for the greater good of the team.**

I can still imagine that you think The Featherlight Boys was a big exception: 'Those kinds of teams only exist in student sport.' But I don't believe we were such an exception. There are definitely teams that win while the members lose, or even win *thanks to* the loss of the members.

A telling example is the 22nd regiment of the US Army – a regiment consists of roughly three thousand men. In November 1944 the 22nd was deployed in the Hürtgenwald in the Eifel Mountains, fighting the Germans. During the day there were fatalities, which were replaced at night – a large number of fatalities. Every night trucks full of new recruits arrived. The new arrivals were often sent immediately into the front line and the next night more new trucks moved up to the front. Soldiers who lasted a few days soon made sergeant, or higher, because sergeants also bought it in the woods. In 18 days – the length of the battle of Hürtgenwald – 2,800 of the three thousand men died. But they did win, the 22nd. Wow, what a success: they beat the Germans.

The reason the 22nd regiment finally beat the Germans resides precisely in that strategy of hurling ever more new troops into the fray: the Germans couldn't handle it. Yet the question remains: who actually won? Not those soldiers, because none of them was left at the end of the war. Of the three thousand, some thirteen thousand perished between June 1944 and May 1945. I beg your pardon? Thirteen thousand of the three thousand?! Exactly: the complete 22nd regiment was wiped out four times. They're still proud of it in 'the 22nd' now they're fighting in Iraq, proud of 'their' victory without knowing exactly whose victory it was.

One of the saddest victims of the Hürtgenwald was Eddie Slovik, not a member of the 22nd but of the 28th, another regiment that was wiped out a number of times in a few months. Eddie Slovik didn't feel like being hurled into battle for the success of the regiment. Eddie Slovik deserted. And who can blame him? But he became the only US soldier in World War II to receive the maximum punishment for desertion: the death penalty. I identify with Eddie Slovik. In his place I would have done the same. The success of the group is surely a rather intangible success when every member of that group is wiped out.

As I write it strikes me that the years when I was rowing covered a fairly exceptional period of my life. I'm not really one for team sports, and I wasn't before I took up rowing. I'm not much of a sportsman at all, I think. Sport is so often about winning, and I've always a rather ambivalent relationship with winning. It's not that I have a fear of failure and don't dare win, but whenever I'm on the point of winning – whatever the sport or game – I start wondering what winning is needed for. Every winner requires a loser and I find myself automatically empathising with the loser. Why should I actually want to win?

The winner is acclaimed. Of course: who else would be acclaimed? Number two? Number seven? So it might as well be number one. If it had been number seven we'd have tried to be number seven. That would have been the winner. Because we certainly want to be acclaimed. It's great. But is winning itself really so nice? And why should we only acclaim the winner? Why not include the loser too more often? Is there something wrong with him or her?

I want to win because I can't want to lose. If I wanted to lose, I would win if I'd lost, and so be a winner after all. Furthermore: winner takes all, but what does the winner actually 'take', then? Sometimes it's obvious: when two people race for a cake the first one to reach it, the winner, eats the cake up. That's something worthwhile: a cake. Or when there are thirteen candidates for one job. In that case it's so nice beating the other twelve, but often we only want to win in order to be better than the other person. I have difficult understanding that. Where's the fun in that?

Winning is wired into us. The spermatozoon I came from was a winner. Number one in a race with several hundred million other spermatozoa. And the spermatozoon from which my father originated was also a winner. My father is a winner in all respects, as is my mother: for surviving their childhoods and finding each other. Their parents – exactly the same sort of winners. For hundreds and thousands of successive generations not one of my forefathers died in childhood – while all around them people were dying in droves. Millions of years ago, when my great–great–great–grandmother was a kind of salamander, she was the one who survived, alone of all her brothers and sisters. A winner.

I'm the end of a chain of millions of successive winners. That puts me under pressure: must I be a winner too? As a kind of obligation to the winners before me?

Winning goes on; the winner achieves success. 'Success' in the meaning of 'that which goes on'. But is winning good in itself? Or to put it more clearly: Is winning good *for the winner too*?

Right, so I have an ambivalent relationship with winning. Even at primary school we played football to win, or at any rate my classmates did. They liked winning, while I found a nice game of football more than enough. At some point in year four we had a very good football team. That was no thanks to me, though. We played against other teams in our school and against teams from other local schools. We usually won.

'Couldn't we occasionally lend one of our best players to the other side?' I once suggested at the time. 'If everyone hates losing so much, and if it's inevitable that there are winners and losers, can't we spread the suffering a little more evenly?' It struck me as a logical and excellent plan, but my classmates saw things differently. They thought I was a wally, or didn't quite get it, and so we went on winning, and I was left with a sometimes triumphant, but sometimes ambivalent feeling.

Years later my time finally came. In the reception class at secondary school during a PE lesson. I was in class 11 and we had PE at the same time as class 12. The classes were often mixed and we played the occasional game and jumped the vaulting horse together. At some point in the summer the two PE teachers organised a large-scale relay race. The ten fastest runners from class 12 had to race against our ten fastest runners. Though I wasn't much good at football, I could run. We were each to run a circuit of a kilometre – I think the whole PE hour was set aside for the relay race.

We got off to a good start – I remember it very well. In our class there was a tall guy who'd had to stay down a year and who I think had failed a reception class elsewhere. In any case he was a lot bigger and stronger than most of my class-mates and he could also run a lot faster. Thanks to him and a few others we were soon almost half a circuit ahead, and the moment approached when I would have to start, as runner number eight, towards the end.

I stood nervously at the start of the course waiting for my predecessor to tap me on the back, and exactly at the right moment I started running as fast as my legs could carry me: 100 metres, 200 metres. Until after about 300 metres I started to wonder what I was actually doing.

'Hey, Bas,' I thought, 'here I am running very, very fast. Running's all right, but you have to go very fast and I think a whole kilometre is a bit far. Why am I taking part in all this? I wondered, while trying to go on running as fast as possible. 'If I go on racing as fast as this we'll win the relay, but I'll get out of breath and furthermore I'll disappoint the people in class 12. In fact I have two choices: run myself into the ground so that my class wins the race, or continue calmly at my own speed and see what happens.' Probably losing is what would happen. 'Run very fast and make ten people lose; or run less fast and make ten other people lose. That's what it boils down to,' I reflected. And as I reflected I started running slower and slower until finally finished my kilometre at a comfortable jog – to the astonishment, and fury, of my classmates.

However hard I tried subsequently to explain my dilemma, I wasn't understood: 'But you're running for your own class, aren't you, you dope? Not for the other lot!

'But why? Why should I want my own class to win rather than that other class? There are always ten winners and ten losers. What difference does it make? Furthermore in one case I have to run myself into the ground and in the other case I run at my own pace. If the result of both options doesn't make any difference – ten winners and ten losers – why should I run myself into the ground?'

The pupils of class 12, though, couldn't make head or tail of it either and although they were happy with the victory that had fallen into their lap, they thought I was just a nutter. But for me that didn't detract from the genuineness of my dilemma.

What was going on? How was it that I thought so differently about these things than my classmates and my fellow-pupils from class 12? Was I mad perhaps? Was I wrong or was I overlooking something?

I don't actually think I was – or am – mad. Although you must never trust anyone who says they're not mad: the greatest madman says the same. My reasoning at that time was rock solid. If you have to choose between two alternatives: running very fast so that ten people win; or running at your pace so that ten other people win; so why should you choose option one? Why are we prepared to run for our own team, even if we have to run faster than is good for us?

Well, we certainly don't all run for our team. Sometimes we shirk it and cut corners, but we think we ought to. Your own team is more important than another team. Why actually? Why is it that we think that? And what's going on with people who think differently about it?

Because we're nice people and care about each other, is a possible answer. But I was no nastier than the rest by not running. I was nice too, except that I was nice to other people. We're certainly not nice to everyone. That's precisely the point. If we were nice to everyone we would have divided losing and winning more fairly.

What I'm driving at is that we are naturally nicer to members of our team than to non-team members. Charity begins at home. Love thy neighbour – but not thy distant neighbour. Perhaps you find or this terribly obvious, but I don't.

There are various stories that explain why it is that we choose our own team and not someone else's team. But one of those stories is that it doesn't work the other way round. Teams comprising only pig-headed guys like me fall apart like grains of sand, like the anarchist group and the student club did. Those kinds of teams lose and disappear, which is why there are few if any such teams. However, that doesn't mean that that they're not nice teams and those pig-headed guys aren't right.

☞ If you have to choose between two alternatives: doing your very best so that your own team wins, and doing less than your best so that another team wins, why should you choose option one?

☞ Teams in which the idea prevails that everyone must do his best for the team win out over teams in which things are rather more relaxed. But are the members of team one also better off?

I sometimes still face the same dilemma as in class 11. When I'm asked to show solidarity with the Netherlands for example, instead of Germany or Zimbabwe, say. I don't really understand. I like to show solidarity with other Dutch people; just as I also feel solidarity with Germans and people from all over. Real people, people who are alive, feel pleasure, suffer pain. I feel solidarity with them. But I don't feel solidarity with the Netherlands. A country is just an idea; it's not people. At times like that I feel a bit of an Eddie Slovik, a deserter.

'If we don't work harder we'll lose out to the Chinese,' said a friend of mine recently. 'I've been there and those people work so hard for so little money. We can never compete with that.'

'What'll happen then, if we lose out against the Chinese? Will we notice the difference?'

'Well, our generation probably won't. Things like that take a while. But give it a few decades and the Chinese will be more prosperous than we are.'

'Prosperity. What good will it do them, those Chinese? What kind of thing can they buy with that prosperity that Dutch people won't be able to but would like to have?'

'Health care, security, pension, a social security system. It all has to be paid for and if we don't roll our sleeves up the Chinese will soon have those and we won't any longer — by "we" I mean the Dutch, that is.'

'So I've got to start working harder, longer, or start working for less money to prevent the Chinese from having more prosperity than the Dutch in the near future?'

'Exactly, yes, surely you wouldn't want...?'

'But I don't know the Dutch people we're talking about. That's not all: the majority of those Dutch people don't even exist yet, they haven't been born. We're talking about the Dutch people of the future. What's the difference between Dutch people who don't yet exist and Chinese who don't yet exist? Why should I roll up my sleeves for one and not for the other? Of course it'll be a terrible shame if the Dutch people of the future no longer have good health care, receive poor education and are frightened about their security, but I can't see why it should be "more of a shame" that this should happen to Dutch people instead of Chinese.

'If I understand correctly I have the choice between scrimping and saving so that Dutch people I don't know and haven't even been born yet enjoy prosperity; or not to scrimp and save so that Chinese I don't know either and haven't been born yet enjoy that prosperity. That doesn't strike me as a difficult choice. I'll choose not to scrimp and save. Everyone is welcome to prosperity, but I see no treason to allow non-existent Dutch people more prosperity than non-existent Chinese. And I'm still not clear why I should roll up my sleeves for that purpose.'

A village in the south of the Netherlands has two societies: the billy-goats and the nanny-goats. They are both bands, that is, brass or marching bands, but they refuse to have anything to do with each other. The village is split down the middle: one half are billy-goats the other nanny-goats. Oddly enough, both billy-goats and nanny-goats are world-class bands.

The village has two bakers (one for the billy-goats and one for the nanny-goats), two butchers and two barbers. 'Don't think a nanny-goat will ever enter this house,' billy-goat fathers shout at their teenage children. 'Billy-goats and nanny-goats don't mix'. If the teenagers listen to their fathers they're automatically confirming that billy-goats and nanny-goats don't mix – and they do listen, because no billy-goat has ever yet married a nanny-goat.

'We nanny-goats are a completely different breed. Calmer and with more feeling for harmony; you can hear it in our music.'

Both societies emphasise their mutual differences and affirm their own specialness. In that way the differences naturally persist, and with them the two societies. But if the villagers were more sensible they would occasionally go to the other baker and intermarry.

That division between billy-goats and nanny-goats may be ridiculous in our eyes. 'Let them all muck in together, what nonsense.' But aren't we caught in the same kind of nonsense? When we cheer for our national team rather than another? Isn't it just the same?

At school we learn the history of our own country – as if our country were something special; we think Beckham is better than Ronaldo; and we can sing 'God Save the Queen' but not the 'Marseillaise'. We're definitely chauvinistic, though we sometimes think we're not.

Foreigners who want to become British citizens have to suffer the indignity of taking courses and suchlike – because you can't become a citizen just like that. And when someone makes it, it's accompanied by ceremonial hooha. Britain and British culture are something special, something special that Britons are proud – or should be proud of. Lots of people think that such pride isn't too bad, and that it could be worse. But imagine if it were even less.

What would happen to our country if we stopped learning about our country? 'Would you rather learn about the Belgian royal family? Fine.' 'Or would you rather speak Chinese than English? Great!' Imagine if we were taught the history of Bolivia at school, or the history of everyone whose surname begins with 'K'. An exciting prospect: Henry Kissinger, Helmut Kohl and Billy Jean King. We would learn that we may live in Britain, but that Britain isn't all that special, that Cheddar cheese is certainly nice, but Roquefort is pretty good too – or Edam. 'Perhaps you should try watching TV in an Italian team shirt,' teacher would say, 'and cheering when Totti scores another goal. Then next week it'll be Brazil.'

I'd like a culture like that. A culture that says: listen hard to what other people from far away have got to say; it's usually really interesting. A modest culture that puts itself into perspective, where a different flag is hoisted every day, of another new country or club; because all those different flags are so nice.

I'm afraid a culture like that won't last very long. Just as the anarchist group and the student club didn't last very long. A culture like that erases itself, as it were, disappears.

It can't be helped. Imagine you wanted to do something about it: 'We shan't let our modest culture that puts itself into perspective disappear just like that. We must learn to be proud of our modest culture. Down with modest!' Modesty would disappear after all.

Like PK chewing gum was doomed to disappear, the wisdom of Mrs Crab disappeared, and the anarchist group disappeared, a modest culture that puts itself in perspective will also disappear from the stage. But I don't like it any the less for that.

The message of the things that disappear can scarcely be heard, like the message of the anarchist group and the student club. The message that you needn't take your own society – or club, organisation, or perhaps even country – so seriously, that it's not the end of the world when a society like that packs up, that you don't need student initiation rituals, that anyone can join, or leave again. That message – which I think is a wise one – is one we scarcely hear, not because it's untrue or not of value, but because it's a message that can't survive. A message that, as it were, erases itself. Yet it's a beautiful message, as far as I'm concerned.

17

A really successful life

Y'know, I came up with a new game show idea recently. It's called the Old Game. You got three old guys with loaded guns on stage. They look back at their lives, see who they were, what they accomplished, how close they came to realizing their dreams. The winner is the one who doesn't blow his brains out. He gets a refrigerator.

CHUCK BARRIS
IN *CONFESSIONS OF A
DANGEROUS MIND*, 2002

I'd promised to make a plausible case to you that we have some similarities to my duck that so fanatically denies herself food while hatching her eggs. My duck that precisely because of this behaviour is part of a continuing chain of such ducks. I hope I've kept my promise. I'm not sure but I think I've shown that there are loads of through roads and that we're a part of them and I've shown that those through roads are not automatically good – at any rate not *for you*. Furthermore I've shown that the non-through roads, the dead ends, can also be splendid thoroughfares.

What would you think if your life was a dead end, a cul-de-sac leading nowhere? What would you think if not one of your ideas was taken up by other people, you had written no books; you hadn't had any children, set up a company; or been a role-model in any way? You're not to be found in any hall of fame, or even in anyone's memory – your life was a dead end. What would you think?

I hope you wouldn't think anything, because dead-end streets can be the nicest streets. At the end of the street where I live there's a right turn to the next village. A three-kilometre dead end. When you get to the village there's nowhere to go. You can go 100 metres to the left, or 100 metres to the right, walk round the church square and that's it. The road to the village is a dead end. It leads to nothing except the village, and from the village the only way is back. But it's a wonderful road. I love walking down it, dawdle a bit when I get to the village and walk back, or take the bus – there's one an hour.

The most beautiful things can be dead ends:

☞ Mrs Crab, that pig-headed fiddler crab that chose differently from the other ladies, was at a dead end. But she was sensible.

☞ PK, precisely because it was such an unassuming chewing gum, was at a dead end.

☞ Biologically, gay people are at a dead end: no posterity for them, but that doesn't detract from the value of their lives.

☞ The culture of finding other cultures as fascinating as one's own does not maintain itself. A dead end. But it is attractive – I think.

☞ Inefficiency is a dead end – efficiency wins – but inefficiency is still very pleasant.

☞ The tip in the Lonely Planet about 'that marvellous bar where no one ever goes' is a dead end. It's true for one edition and after that it's not.

☞ The odd idea of the artist from the new town, that it's perfectly OK for drawings to wash away, will always remain exceptional; it's a dead end. But that doesn't make it any less true.

☞ That Dutch anarchist group was at a dead end. Necessarily. That's why we've forgotten about them. But it was a terrific club.

☞ The message that a lazy life at home is really nice is a dead end, isn't heard. Because a lazybones is too lazy to say anything; but perhaps he's laughing up his sleeve.

☞ **And the idea that you don't have to win, don't have to achieve results or success that spur others on, is a dead end: it will always have to compete with the cacophony of the winners. Success is more infectious than non-success, but certainly not more pleasant in itself.**

All these things are a dead end, but they're wonderful things – all of them.

A while ago I was at the funeral of the father of a friend, Rosalie. It was of course a sad affair, but the father had lived to be about eighty, so it wasn't that bad. 'Father achieved all sorts of things in his life', said Rosalie in her address at the funeral service. 'He had three children – of which I'm one – eight grandchildren and one more on the way. Just after the war he started up a carpentry business with his bare hands, and look what it's grown into. Thirty employees are seated here in church – though Father retired over ten years ago – and the business is still flourishing. After retiring he drove twice in the Paris–Dakar rally. The last time he was actually best amateur in the province in the Nissan category. Father achieved an enormous amount. He did not live for nothing. Father can look back on a very successful life.'

Rosalie didn't say how good – or bad – a time her

father had had, whether he was comfortable in his own skin, picked his nose, sat patiently in tailbacks, or got worked up, took the dog for walks, or got eight hours' sleep a night. We didn't hear that kind of thing: that had nothing to do with success.

Curious really: you spend one third of your life sleeping, completely for yourself. Perhaps that's why 'successful sleeping' or 'a successful holiday' sound rather odd.

The successful person seems enviable. The spermatozoon from which I came was successful. It came first in a race with between 100 and 200 million other spermatozoa – the winner. I don't find it easy to identify with sperm, but if I have to I prefer the winner to the losers, which swam a few aimless circuits around my mother's body.

The fact that all those spermatozoa are striving for the same thing doesn't mean that what they are striving for is good for them. If in a village somewhere all the young men try once a year to steal the tip of the church spire and scramble en masse up the walls of the church, that can mean one of two things: there's either something really special about that tip, or the young men are slightly crazy. On the assumption that the tip is not that special, I'll go for option two and envy not the winner, but the young men who stood and watched at a distance, shrugging their shoulders and looking at all the commotion while drinking another mouthful of their beer. But no fame for them, no photos in the bar, no success.

The winning spermatozoon derives very little benefit from its success. While the losers swam their circuits – for as long as three days – the winner had already disappeared, swallowed and devoured by the ovum it had just fertilised, dissolved in the dividing new embryo, Bas Haring. Some success.

It seems as if the winner is enviable: the first spermatozoon, the winner whose life has not been in vain. But it didn't do all that well out of it: it lived only a few minutes and the others lived for a few days. Perhaps the losers are more enviable. What would you prefer: to be torn to pieces after a life of a few minutes and so form the link in a chain of success? Or to swim circuits for two or three days without setting anything in motion. I choose option two: I prefer swimming circuits to being torn to pieces.

If all the spermatozoa swim as fast as possible in order to be first, then it seems as if the only one that succeeds is to be envied. But perhaps that one spermatozoon is on the contrary a victim, sacrificing itself in order to make a new future possible. Like a kind of Jesus Christ who alone took all the sins of the future on himself, so that the others could get on with business as usual.

Of course, success goes on – that is already implicit in the etymology of the word – but is the person who achieves success to be envied...?

By analogy with sperm I wonder what life is most to be envied. The life aimlessly swimming circuits – nice and calmly and for a nice long time – or the life that has set something in motion, the successful life. If I were to be consistent I'd opt for the former, but I don't. I don't quite know why. I write books, appear on TV and lecture. I set all kinds of things in motion, but I take my hat off to the person who has no need for any of this. Who has no need for a successful life. Hats off to mothers and fathers at whose funeral there is nothing to say except that he or she slept well, had a salt-water aquarium and adored curry.